INTEGRATED
COST
REDUCTION

INTEGRATED

COST

Ron Nussle, Jr.

Jim Morgan

REDUCTION

Reed

Business Press

INTEGRATED COST REDUCTION

A *Purchasing® Magazine* Book
Published by Reed Press ™
360 Park Avenue South
New York, NY 10010

www.reedpress.com

Library of Congress Cataloging-in-Publication Data

Nussle, Ron,
   Integrated cost reduction / Ron Nussle, Jr. & Jim Morgan.
      p. cm.
   ISBN 1-59429-013-X (hardcover : alk. paper)
   1. Cost control. 2. Industrial productivity—Cost effectiveness. 3. Industrial
efficiency. I. Morgan, Jim, 1928– II. Title.
   HD47.3.N87 2004
   658.15'52—dc22

                                                              2004007067

Designed by John Reinhardt Book Design

Printed in the United States

10 9 8 7 6 5 4 3 2 1

To Jesus Christ
whose "golden rule" is the foundation
of my business philosophy—and of the concepts in this book.
And to my wife, Suzanne, who encouraged me to listen to Him.

100% of my royalties from this book will be donated to charity.

Ron Nussle, Jr.

CONTENTS

Chapter 3: Overview of the ICR Process   55

Overview—or ICR in action. A look at the potential payoffs of
ICR and a discussion of what's needed to set up an ICR system
in a company. The five phases that companies have to march
through on the way to mounting a successful ICR program. A
program for speedy implementation.

PART II
ICR PROCESS EXECUTION STEPS
FOR PRACTITIONERS AND PROJECT MANAGERS

Chapter 4: Engaging Senior Management   69

What top managers need to be told and shown to convince
them that ICR is really a good idea. The areas that will need
close documentation—market potential, progran requirements,
current costs, new cost targets, supplier participation, program
feasibility.

Chapter 5: Preparation   87

A look at the kinds of information that will need to be collected
prior to the actual implementation of an ICR process. The depth
of data needed and what to do if your company cannot supply
data at any great depth.

Chapter 6: Supplier Engagement Overview   95

A look at where this program is leading in terms of how supplier
engagement-buyer relationships will change. Affect on things
like total market potential, customer flow down requirements,
new product cost targets, objectives. The mechanics of setting
supplier engagement in place.

Chapter 7: Supplier Engagement in Design   109

Supplier engagement in design. Implementation of VA/VE principles to enhance value to the customer. A look at how the old

principles of function analysis can be broadened to achieve more
design to cost objectives.

Chapter 8: Supplier Engagement in Manufacturing and Six Sigma   125

Supplier engagement in manufacturing. A look at the marriage
of lean manufacturing principles and those of VA/VE to eliminate waste, improve quality, and reduce cycle time. A look at the
objectives and the deliverables.

Chapter 9: Engagement Supply Chain and E-Procurement   135

Supplier engagement in e-procurement. A look at the new procurement tools and strategies ro achieve cost reductions. An
evaluation of of their overall significance. A hard-headed look at
e-procurement strategies and tools and their potential to achieve
the overall cost reduction target.

Chapter 10: Creating the Plan   151

Integrating and priortizing supplier engagement recommendations. An examination of the process for selecting which proposals get implemented, which get put on hold. How to keep the
selection process objective and effective.

Chapter 11: Implementation and Lessons Learned   163

Execution. How to use program management to realize planned
improvements. Development of an implementation flow diagram—from documentation to program concurrence, to work
plan. to supplier work plan.

Epilogue   169

Summary and review. How to evaluate whether the project was
a success or failure. Matching accomplishments to objectives.

Appendix   171

Case studies

INTEGRATED
COST
REDUCTION

INTRODUCTION

THIS IS A BOOK written for those who are concerned about costs. It is written for executives and practitioners who recognize that cost reduction is at the center of enterprise-wide competitiveness. It is also written for those who want a non-technical explanation of the components of cost and cost reduction and some suggestions on how to set up a systematic approach to cost reduction.

The approach we use is called *Integrated Cost Reduction* (ICR). It is predicated on the fact that no matter how innovative a company's products, forceful its marketing, efficient its production, how well it does all the things that good companies are supposed to do, it will not be as truly competitive as it could be until it understands how to reduce the drivers of its own cost structure. Only when companies fully understand their cost drivers are they ready to take significant action to reduce costs.

"Great!" you say, "Just what the country needs—another new management theory to add to the management buzzword boneyard." In anticipation of some such lack of enthusiasm, we readily concede the obvious overabundance in the past five decades or so of management theories aimed at improving industrial competitiveness. Indeed, we also concede that most have gone the way of the albatros.

In most cases early demise was for good reason! Many, (maybe most) competitiveness theories were doomed from the start for lack of universal applicability. Many more turned out to be little more than metaphors for working hard and reaping well earned rewards for the hard work. A few, however, have proven themselves over the years and delivered legitimate results (and give ICR its results: Lean Manufacturing, Six Sigma, Value Analysis, Value Engineering and Supply Chain Management.

One question that deserves an answer is, "Why does the business world go through one fad after another trying to improve their competitiveness?" One popular answer is that the problem lies with managers searching for silver bullets that apply "single-point solutions" to very complex problems. Managers appear to be grasping for individual solutions to individual problems or, on the other hand, looking for ways to apply a single solution or method to a host of problems. In the first case, they fail to see the relationship of one problem to others in the company or its systems. In the second case they're attempting to use solutions that have only limited applications.

Most of the celebrated solutions for responding to global competition are severely limited in scope and effectiveness. They often were stand-alone solutions created by quality, manufacturing, or supply chain professionals to solve problems and improve competitiveness within their own "functional castles."

Unfortunately most had little universal application. Many, in fact, may have made sense when used as part of a unified philosophy or strategy (such as TQM), but not when applied separately.

Since typical manufacturing companies have 70–80% of their costs in purchased materials, most *Fortune 500* companies have responded to global price pressures by launching corporate supply chain initiatives. As reported in the literature, these companies' cost savings are achieved from four primary methods of cost reduction: re-negotiation/supplier leveraging; global sourcing; use of exchanges; and use of e-auctions. Each of these has its potentially negative side effects. A comparison of these side effects looks like this:

- Re-negotiation, by itself, is typically just "margin transfer" with four potential and often unintended, results: Suppliers recover their losses during the next upturn; Suppliers recover their losses by lowering Engineering Investment, service and/or quality levels; Suppliers don't give their best cost reduction ideas up-front during design, but save them for a future negotiation; Suppliers don't recover their losses and exit the industry.
- Global sourcing is a great way to lower costs, but takes huge investments in time and resources before break-even occurs.
- Exchanges have failed to generate any substantive cost savings are almost all collapsing.
- E-auctions are another form of "win-lose" negotiations (in most cases, but there are some rare exceptions).

Despite all of our up-front negative concessions about the general effectiveness of management theories, we make no concessions about ICR. It is founded on the proven process elements that have been used by at least three *Fortune 500* companies to achieve highly successful results in cost reduction:

- AlliedSignal, which began ICR in 1995 and merged with Honeywell in 1998, has chalked up $millions in savings to date.
- Honeywell, which since its merger with AlliedSignal, has continued to achieve $millions in savings from ICR.
- Cessna, which began ICR in 2001, and is also seeing 7-figure savings so far.

What gives ICR strength is its focus on bringing together the proven processes of value analysis/value engineering, lean manufacturing, Six Sigma, supply chain management, and e-commerce under one seamless cost reduction umbrella.

In any case, the thrust of this book is not on individual stand-alone solutions, but on a step-by-step approach to solving a single but very complex problem facing companies across the country—cost reduction. Specifically, we make the case for the development of a discipline that companies can use to systematically take costs out of their operations at many levels at the same time.

However, while our emphasis is on cost, we make this caveat: This book about integrated cost is not a tome for nickel nursers. (Nor is it a collection of good ideas for cutting costs, or a theoretical treatise.) Integrated cost reduction is a thoroughly reasoned approach for systematically questioning costs at every level in an organization and then, once they are understood, finding ways to eliminate redundancies and reduce costs. ICR provides a methodical, step-by-step path to follow.

An important premise around which ICR is structured is that those using it must take an enterprise-wide approach to reducing cost in order to reach the competitiveness demanded by stakeholders (shareholders, customers, management). In the past the traditional approach has been to take a single initiative to solve a cost problem. Unfortunately, solving a single cost problem or making an improvement in only one area can in itself be a recipe for failure.

Studies show that most single-approach improvement processes often require substantial investments in time, resources, and capital before return on investment starts to show up. Break-even time is often delayed and/or disappointing when it does arrive. Some typical examples from various studies:

IMPROVEMENT PROCESS	LEAN MANUFACTURING	SIX SIGMA	E-AUCTIONS
Benchmark company(s)	Pratt & Whitney	Motorola/ Honeywell	GE
What must happen before lower costs actually hit bottom line?	Create cell with 100% of parts flowing. Deplete all "non-flow" WIP.	Chg. design, tooling, and/or process. Set new part effectivity	Plan/hold E-auction. Qualify, Select, transition parts to winner
Typical time to implement (locally)	6–9 mo. per cell	12–16 mo. per part/assembly	12–18 mo. per supplier
Typical total time to implement	18 mo–4 yr (plantwide)	4–6 yr, (plant-wide)	4–6 yr to develop totally new supply base
Typical gross reported savings	5–15% (labor) 20–40 (inventory)	5–15%	10–40%
Typical costs	$–millions	$–millions	costs 25–35% of year's purch. value to qualify a new supplier

ICR uses a broader, more fundamental, approach to cost that takes into consideration such factors as engineering, supply, design, marketing, and production. Unlike the one-shot approaches noted above, ICR moves from very specific to general principles. It is geared to spot patterns, themes, and pockets of information as attention is shifted from department to department throughout a company.

Especially important to the ICR process is how it integrates the proven "best-of-the-best" business improvement processes: Six Sigma in quality, value analysis/value engineering in design and purchasing, lean manufacturing in production, and supply chain management and E-procurement tools in procurement, production, and logistics.

ICR moves across functions and integrates the various initiatives and tools into an overall cost reduction approach. In elementary terms ICR can be said to take four tactics and a number of e-procurement tools and builds them into a strategy or process for spotting cost reduction problems, evaluating solutions, and uncovering cost reduction opportunities

The first tactic, VA/VE, focuses on design changes to lower direct labor and raw materials. The second, lean manufacturing, focuses on "conversion costs" and the waste of queues and set-up time. The third tactic, Six Sigma, focuses on reducing variation and the resulting costs of poor quality (COPQ) in the form of scrap, rework, and repair wastes. The fourth tactic, supply chain re-engineering, focuses on the many opportunities to reduce costs in the supply chain itself. E-procurement tools home in on the opportunities to achieve cost reductions that are available to improve the procurement and supply management operations of the organization.

Again, what sets ICR apart from any one of these tactics is that it integrates all of the separate tactics into a strategy or process for cost reduction. More important, it achieves more substantial overall product cost reductions than could ever be approached by using the individual tactics, separately.

ICR makes it possible for companies to use all of these tactics and tools simultaneously in an integrated process and as a consequence actually reduce product costs by 10%, 20%, or more—where application of each of the tactics individually can produce cost reductions of only 2–4% of the product cost. In Chapter One, we will explain why many general managers cannot find the phenomenal cost reductions in their P&L statements that the cost reduction project leaders or consultants claimed in their PowerPoint presentations.

A major danger in trying to apply ICR is that it has to be understood as an enterprise-wide approach. It will not work if it is within a function (e.g. Engineering group or purchasing department). VA/VE, for instance, might ask the question: "Is the product designed to meet the needs of the customer as well as it could be?" In many cases it might immediately get hung up in the design engineering part of the problem. Why? Because VA/VE traditionally tends to restrict itself to product function and product design.

Suppose a company followed the standard VA/VE approach and optimized the design of the part—but still had a traditional "batch and queue" or "push" manufacturing process. Or suppose it really optimized the design and eliminated the unnecessary functions but was still building the product in a circa 1940–50 manufacturing plant with lots of scrap, lots of rework, long set-up times, too much inventory, and great amounts of queue time. The company is still left with the biggest part of the problem—the need to improve manufacturing and quality.

Or let's say the company is still using 1950s style purchasing. As a result, even though it is optimizing the function of the product, it's not buying from the right suppliers, it has not rationalized its supply base (thousands of suppliers building all the pieces), not doing logistics in a cost-effective fashion, not using JIT, and not using all the different supply chain tools that are available. So all it's really doing is optimizing the design features, but 50% of the cost of the product is not even being addressed. Nothing, for instance, is being done about the manufacturing overhead, the purchasing overhead, the engineering overhead, or the quality overhead.

How would the company be able to deal with overhead in ICR? Actually ICR addresses overhead directly. In the above examples ICR practitioners would say, "Forget about changing the design for a while and let's look at such things as volume leveraging with key suppliers or use of more efficient shipping." By working with an integrated system such as ICR, companies can take a more orderly approach to cost reduction.

As noted earlier, this book is not designed to give a comprehensive explanation or history of the ICR process. Rather, it is an attempt at explaining how a few leading companies have integrated all business functions in an enterprise-wide approach to lowering costs.

In essence this is a book within a book. This introduction and the first three chapters make up Part I and are designed to give executives and management a summary explanation of what ICR is and how it affects corporate cost structures when implemented properly. Chapters 4–9 are written for supply chain practitioners and project managers and explain in fairly complete detail the steps that need to be followed to launch an ICR project. These chapters are meant to appeal to the needs of middle managers who will put the principles of ICR to work in their companies. Chapter 10 helps the ICR practitioner priortize which cost reduction ideas get implemented, Chapter 11 with integrating and execution—using program management to realize the planned improvements, and Chapter 12 is a summary and review of the subject that looks at this question: Did we achieve our objectives? The Appendix contains actual case studies, which go into even greater depth with examples of four different types of ICR projects:

1. New product focused
2. Business/e-procurement focused
3. Design focused
4. Manufacturing and quality process improvement focused

WHAT'S DIFFERENT ABOUT ICR?

- It's a proven process at three *Fortune 500* companies (AlliedSignal, Honeywell, Cessna Aircraft Co.).
- It's WIN-WIN and suppliers love it.
- It's FASTER (and) SAFER than moving parts to a new supplier.
- It's IMPORTANT to managers who still need "quality parts on time."
- ICR can achieve 5–15% COST REDUCTION and not destroy relationships with proven, long-term suppliers.

PART I

ICR SUMMARY
AND RESULTS
FOR EXECUTIVES
AND MANAGEMENT

1

WHAT ICR IS ALL ABOUT

EXECUTIVE SUMMARY: Integrated cost reduction (ICR) is a process that takes a number of tools and applies them in a strategic way to solve a growing problem in American business: cost reduction. At the heart of ICR is the combination of five of the best-known business management tools into a cohesive strategy or process. What is achieved by this combination of tools is the capability of achieving cost reductions that literally dwarf those obtainable through the use of one of the tools individually. Indeed, in many cases, the use of the ICR process is capable of achieving cost savings not thought possible.

The five tools, which will be discussed at greater length in Chapter 2, are lean manufacturing, the Six Sigma process, value analysis/value engineering, supply chain management, and e-procurement. Using the five tools in an intelligently designed and implemented program can produce cost reduction processes of unusual sophistications.

In simple terms ICR brings a new focus to the way cost reduction is approached within an organization. The following from-to examples demonstrate the changes that can be expected to take place as the principles of ICR are applied across organizations:

FROM	TO
Demands for specific supplier price cuts	Joint supplier-customer efforts to achieve cost reductions
Use of negotiation to beat down prices	Joint customer-supplier analysis of cost factors
Use of single tool to probe costs reduction	Use of integrated set of cost tools
Functional initiatives to probe costs probe	Use of integrated initiatives to costs
Investigation of one cost issue at a time	Analysis of how product features affect cost

• • •

GENERAL MANAGERS IN MANUFACTURING companies have always had it tough. Customers have always wanted their goods and services delivered "better, faster, and cheaper." Now the Internet allows unprecedented world-wide access to instantaneous information and global competition is accelerating. In this milieu customers' expectations are skyrocketing, and capital is flowing from traditional businesses to "new economy" business models. Stock prices for manufacturing companies have not kept pace with software, computer, or bio-technology companies and general managers are being forced to continuously improve annual productivity and cash flow while fending off unprecedented global competition and increased costs for labor, facilities, and environmental regulation.

It's in this environment that the goal for "improved value" has come to mean dramatically different things to the general manager's two key stakeholders—shareholders and customers. The two conflicting definitions of value (see Figure 1-1) drive a general manager to two completely different action sets at the same time. The customer wants more goods and services, for lower and lower prices each year. If the company gives the customers what they want, they may see costs and assets increase to deliver more features, more service, more support, and no waiting—all at a lower price. While the investment market, with its increased focus on profit and assets, wants "more profit with less investment," shareholders celebrate when a company increases revenue while simultaneously laying off employees, closing plants, and slashing overhead.

In plain terms general managers can no longer focus on "quality" or "cost" or "delivery" or "better designs"—one at a time. Rather, they must focus on each simultaneously. ICR spans numerous organizations to bring a cross-functional process to lower costs, while simultaneously improving product quality, delivery, and service. This is what separates ICR from "silver bullets" that have left so many general managers wishing they were the departed consultants that were paid to implement these processes and leave the general manager to clean up the collateral damage.

BOGUS SAVINGS?

On the latter point it needs to be pointed out that many of the savings numbers being quoted for e-auctions, global sourcing, etc., need some close examination. In many cases double-digit savings are being quoted for e-auction savings before projects employing e-auctions or reverse auctions have actually been

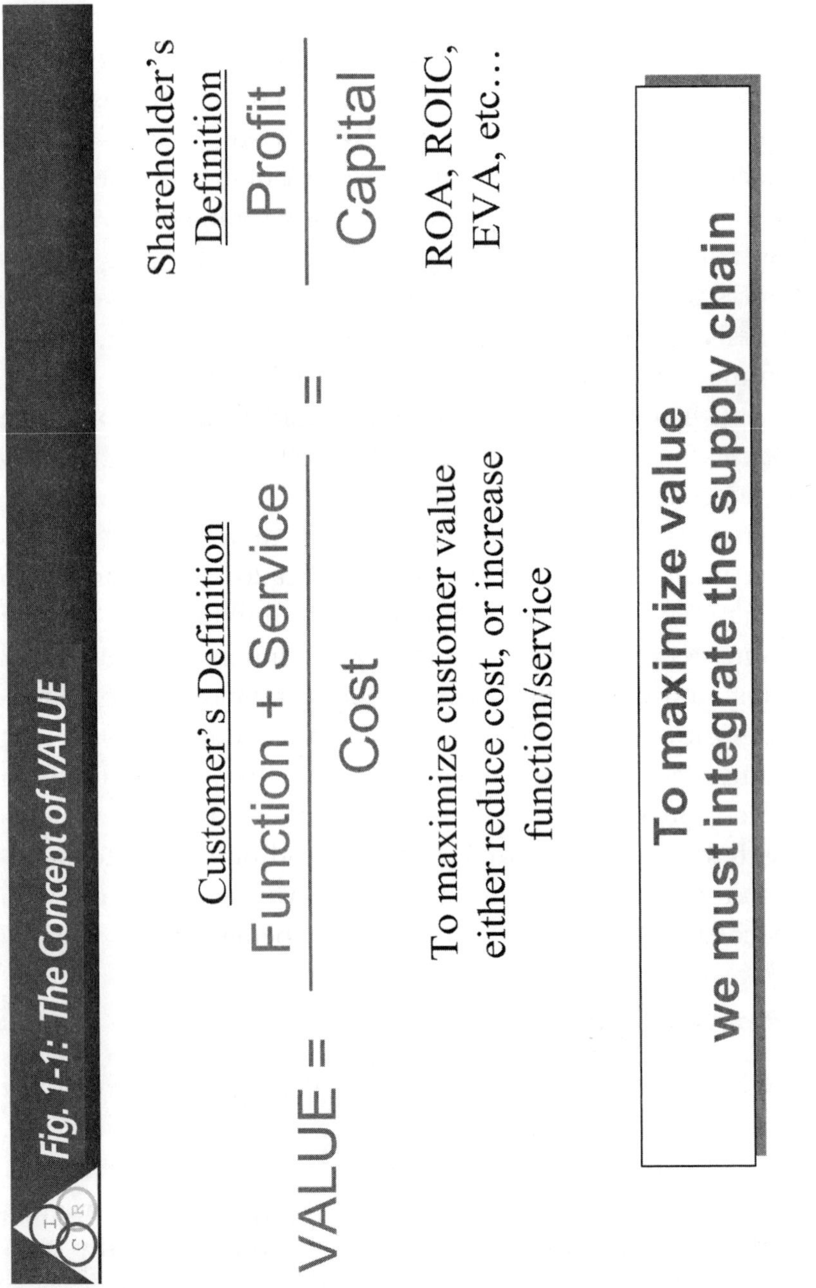
Fig. 1-1: The Concept of VALUE
Customer's Definition
VALUE =
Function + Service
Cost
=
Shareholder's
Definition
Profit
Capital
To maximize customer value
either reduce cost, or increase
function/service
ROA, ROIC,
EVA, etc…
To maximize value
we must integrate the supply chain

implemented and parts been moved. So the question has to be, "Are these gross savings or net savings?" In most cases the answer is "they're gross savings." Indeed, many members of executive management would be greatly surprised to find out after they've moved parts to lower cost domestic suppliers or moved parts overseas—Poland or China, for example—there are no savings left.

This is measurable. For instance, benchmark data have shown repeatedly that the logistics and management cost of using a global supplier are 20–30% higher than the cost of a domestic supplier. Upon examining global supply chain and logistics costs, more than one study has found that unless 20–30% savings is achieved, it's not even worth considering global sourcing. Say for instance, you quote a domestic supplier and a supplier in China and you get 20% better pricing on a particular part. The Chinese supplier would actually be more expensive because logistics costs and duties are very high in China. In another example, a manufacturer moved components from near Shanghai (in the north) to Guangdong (in the south) and saw more than ten tariffs applied as the part moved across various boundaries.

(Note: A 20–30% global sourcing add-on assumes that the supplier is located overseas and the final assembly operations are in North America. This is known as being a "multi-national company." A multi-national company operates in numerous regions, but each region is not necessarily autonomous. A global company, on the other hand, operates, designs, builds, and ships from an overseas location to an overseas customer base. The savings from sourcing, assembling, and shipping all from the same location are obvious. The down-side of this strategy, of course, is the tremendous time and effort (typically years and millions of dollars) required to develop this global capability and ensuring that the same level of quality and customer service is available from a remote facility. Nevertheless, IBM, GE, Ford, Caterpillar, and others have successfully accomplished this.)

If the American supplier came in at $100, unless the Chinese supplier could beat his price by at least 20–30% the American customer is better off going to the American supplier after factoring in the effect of transportation; overseas phone calls; travel costs to China to solve quality and reliability problems; manufacturing problems, delays in shipping (it often takes weeks or months to receive a part vs. North America where it's possible to get almost any part from a supplier in North America in 2–3 days or less. It's almost impossible to get from China to the U.S. in less than two weeks. The point: It's very easy for someone to quote savings of 20–30% on parts coming out of China when in reality 30% equals 0%. There's no savings at all because they are reporting gross savings rather than net savings. After all the transition costs are subtracted, it is easy to see 20–30% cost savings simply evaporate! The good news is that a number of companies that have moved into global sourcing prudently and with their eyes open have reaped substantial benefits.

Similar things can be said about reverse auctions and e-procurement. It's easy to quote 15% or 20% savings, but if the company or supplier haven't built new tools, they haven't paid the cost that it takes to move the parts, paid logistics and transportation costs, paid for first article inspections to be done, haven't paid cancellation charges they may incur from existing suppliers, haven't paid for work in process inventories, etc. Many executives should have listened to their grandfathers' advice, "If it seems too good to be true it probably isn't true."

ICR'S ORIGINS

ICR is a child of desperation. It was born in a period of deep cost cutting in the early 1990s. A new critical fact of life in the form of global competitiveness was striking out at corporate America. Companies were finding themselves backed into corners by customers demanding steep pricing reductions even as they backed their own suppliers into corners with similar demands. Demands for price reductions of 20%, 25%, and more were regularly being tossed across the negotiating table. The aerospace manufacturing industry was particularly hard hit as the nine major airlines lost more than $12 billion in a three-year period (1991–93).

Since these demands were being made at a time when typical supplier margins were barely in the 5–10% range, it took no great genius to see where all of these demands for price cuts were leading. Many companies, especially those engaged in supplying large OEMs, were negotiating their margins away in what was euphemistically referred to as "margin transfer." In such situations suppliers' margins start descending toward zero while customers' margins hold steady or expand—short term. There are three long-term options: (1) the suppliers begin moving resources away from their "losing accounts," while quality, on-time delivery, and responsiveness suffers; (2) the supplier eventually exits the business and the customer company faces the loss of a key supplier; or (3) the market swings back to a "sellers' market," and the supplier regains all (and more) of its lost margins. (Note: During the 1994–1996 Aerospace boom, the surviving suppliers regained much of their previous price concessions when capacity became constrained.)

By the early 1990s the ultimate outcome was beginning to be reached. Growing numbers of suppliers in the aerospace

Fig. 1-2: Why we need an integrated approach

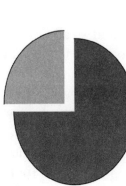

Typical Supplier's Margin

Global Competition Mandated Reduction

Supplier's Cost

Current Product Price

Negotiation alone will not yield required cost reductions

industry, specifically, were falling behind competitively and gradually going out of business. Even the large OEMs were feeling the pain. As their global competition heated up, they were gradually running out of suppliers who were willing or able to continue eating costs.

In this competitive squeeze an important economic fact of life was being written across the nation's industrial landscape for all to see. The lesson: That truly significant reductions in costs are difficult or impossible to bring about strictly at the negotiating table. Demands by a customer that a supplier reduce prices is a short-term tactic at best and will usually collapse on itself unless true reductions in costs are fully implemented.

OTHER LESSONS LEARNED

The fact that true cost reduction is unachievable through negotiation is only one of the lessons. There were, of course, a number of lessons being learned in the competitive days of the last decade of the twentieth century. Among the ones that had the most to do with the evolution of ICR are these:

- **Process vs. Functional Organizations.** For some reason it took a while for many businesses to grasp the reality that a few people or a few functions can't bring about re-engineering initiatives. The fact that "breakthrough" goals require aggressive and innovative responses from all organizations in a company was slow to catch on. One discipline or one or two functions in a company are not sufficient to bring about major changes in corporate performance.
- **Supply chain.** An underlying integrated supply chain strategy is needed to achieve the level of cost reduction demanded by management. In addition to enthusiasm, it

takes close participation and cooperation among managers, functions, and departments.

- **Commodity teams.** In many companies—especially those engaged in manufacturing—commodity teams need to be established to implement corporate-wide materials management strategies. What's more, these teams need to part of an integrated product development and support system.
- **Program Management.** A focused, disciplined approach is required to achieve executive management's very tough quality, cost, and delivery goals.

HOW ICR USES ITS TOOLS

ICR zeros in on the lessons enumerated above and attempts to deal with cost reduction using a carefully thought-out step-by-step analysis of each factor in the value equation, making a finding, and then moving to the next logical step. From analyzing the product, ICR moves on to analyzing the business and defining what the value is that's being added.

For instance, ICR is considerably broader than the usual value analysis/value engineering approach that focuses most of its activity on the product's function. In ICR the lean manufacturing tool often is added to VA/VE. The net result is that the scope of cost reduction is vastly broadened to include all the cost considerations involved in making the product.

Even if a product is designed exactly as it has traditionally been in the past, the addition of lean manufacturing to the ICR mix, can greatly increase the potential for reducing the costs involved in making the product. Moreover, lean manufacturing processes often can be used to improve the quality of a product by eliminating scrap and re-work without actually changing the function of the product or any of its components. In other words, one key to the success of ICR is the integrated thinking that takes place in analyzing product costs.

SOME COSTS ARE REALLY PRICES!

Another important key to successful cost reduction is understanding the difference between prices and costs. This is a stumbling block for a great many people involved in looking to use potential cost-cutting tools. Simply put, they have great difficulty distinguishing between cost and price. For instance, while it is quite fashionable these days to tout such e-procurement tools as on-line "reverse auctions" as cost-cutting tools, in most cases they are really about price.

In most cases, on-line or reverse auctions don't do anything to costs. What they really do is lower prices by increasing competition. This is good so long as the price is not allowed to become the sole criterior for awarding business. When the bidding is allowed to degenerate to a level at which the bid gets awarded solely on the basis of the desparation of the bidders, very little is accomplished.

What is happening in many cases is that a growing number of companies are using some relatively complex business tools (e.g. the internet, supplier relationship management or SRM software, etc.) to accomplish some relatively unsophisticated tactics. These very powerful tools could be used to integrate information across functional silos to facilitate advances in product cost reduction.

Many of these functions (e.g. purchasing, engineering, finance, etc.) tend to be run by management who came up through the ranks within their own function (e.g. accountant, manager, controller, CFO). As a result many good cost reducing initiatives fail to yield proper results because they don't get integrated across the business.

While ICR works best in companies that have cross-functional supply chain teams, we will work from the premise that full integration across functional silos will be less than complete in most companies attempting ICR. While we do advocate that companies should work towards achieving full cross-functional integration for their overall competitiveness in today's global economy, but do not expect or require that to occur prior to launching ICR. The ultimate solution for many companies will probably involve considerable amounts of training and reorganizing—taking all functionally oriented managers and training them to work cross functionally. In the Appendix we list four case studies that show how an ICR process can be implemented in six-eight weeks and deliver dramatic results.

SYSTEMIC APPROACH NEEDED

While product cost often appears to be a single factor, it is actually made up of a number of components. Indeed, one of the reasons for the new interest in ICR is the growing realization that no single product cost element is capable of yielding the kinds of cost savings demanded by global competition (e.g. China).

Typically costs run the gamut of raw materials, manufacturing direct labor costs, manufacturing overhead costs, cost of quality, general and administrative costs, special processes, R&D, and margin. What's more, these different cost components are the product of more than one process—most notably the design process, procurement, and the manufacturing assembly process. Changes in any one of these processes is usually echoed in each of the others.

In manufacturing, for instance, lean manufacturing projects, by themselves will reduce non value added labor costs, but are not sufficient for achieving overall targeted cost reductions. The reason is quite simple: Direct labor for complex products is typically only 10–25% of cost of goods sold (COGS). By only pursuing a lean manufacturing strategy, a company would ignore the major portions of the COGS by failing to examine the design that drives the overhead, rework, and quality costs.

What ICR brings to the cost reduction scene is integrated cost reduction thinking. Next, let's examine value engineering or, design-to-cost (DTC) which traditionally results in focusing on the most obvious cost savings and often ignoring the really important sources of cost reduction. Typically value analyzers would say, "let's evaluate this feature or component of the product. It contains an hour's worth of machining time, but with the use of less complex geometry or simpler materials it's possible to reduce the labor or materials by 10%." As Figure 1-3 shows, the final impact on on total product COGS is less than 3%.

In celebrating the above "10% labor savings, value analyzers were effectively achieving an overall 3% product cost reduction. But, in so doing, they also ignored such wastes as fifteen hours of waiting time endemic to that particular manufacturing process. And this is what separates ICR from most other approaches to cost reduction. ICR focuses not only on the raw materials and major value added labor cost items but also on the non-value added portion of manufacturing labor costs. While traditional VA/VE techniques are especially good at spotting design to cost opportunities, they often are embarrassingly weak at eliminating waste in the manufacturing process.

Often the non-value added portion of labor is three or four times greater than the value added labor. Thus, while reducing machining time from 60 to 55 minutes through VA/VE is a win, it is not nearly so dramatic as the possibilities of eliminating four or five hours of waste in the manufacturing process.

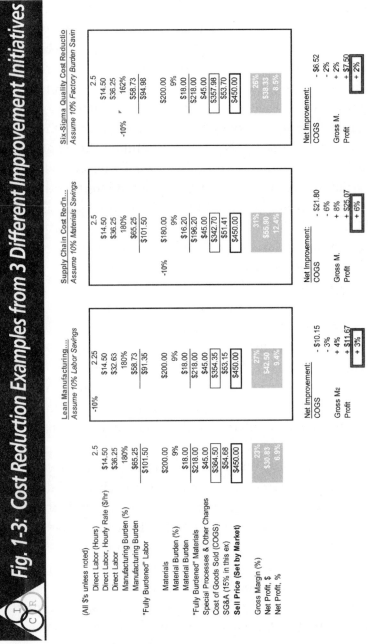

Fig. 1-3: Cost Reduction Examples from 3 Different Improvement Initiatives

COPQ

ICR goes considerably beyond the elimination of non-value added labor in the product. It also attacks head-on the cost of poor quality (COPQ). As companies like GE, Raytheon, and Motorola, who have embraced Six Sigma have realized, COPQ is an often underestimated or unmeasured cost that can have a dramatic effect on a product line's profitability. Six Sigma literature has indicated that the average U.S. supplier has a two to three sigma quality level. This translates into a poor quality cost in the range of 20–30% total revenue! However, typical VA/VE projects do not directly address non-value added labor, and similarly, lean manufacturing projects typically don't take on labor quality improvement. ICR, on the other hand, pays significant attention to both the non-value added portion of labor as well as the waste of cost of poor quality.

SUPPLY CHAIN SAVINGS

Two other ICR process components—supply chain management and e-procurement—represent an area of cost savings that has become the center of much corporate activity in cost and waste elimination. The difference under ICR is that e-procurement and supply chain strategies are used on the supplier's behalf to help them attack cycle time waste, procurement redundancy, and the cost savings possible by volume leveraging. In this way, ICR reduces costs at the source by helping suppliers reduce their largest cost component (materials). The savings can be shared between customer and supplier project, creating a win-win ICR project.

Good examples of the opportunities in this field are found in many industries where the end product is relatively complex—e.g. automotive, aerospace, capital equipment of all types.

Many of the small suppliers that companies work with are $50 million to $70 million companies doing traditional purchasing. They often don't do a good job buying their own special processes or when they're buying materials they may simply not be sophisticated enough in supply management. They don't use strategic sourcing; they don't have long-term agreements or take advantage of commodity leverage.

Typically, many examples can be cited where a number of identical components are needed on a single product yet the supplier ships one component in one box and another in another box at one time. Under the ICR approach the typical questioning in this area would center around determining why the supplier isn't shipping all parts together in one box that goes directly to the assembly line or why aren't suppliers' capabilities more closely screened to take advantage of experience and know-how in a field.

The idea of buying kits from their suppliers may seem elementary, but many may never have been in a position before to consider such an "obvious" solution as kitting. Or the idea of having the supplier drop-ship items just in time may only now make economic sense for the small supplier.

WHEN DOES ICR APPLY?

Thankfully, it is now common knowledge for manufacturing executives that the best time to reduce costs is on new designs during the product development stage. The ICR process has been successfully implemented both on new and mature products. See the case studies in the Appendix for specific examples.

The goals and challenges can be quite different for ICR implementations of new versus mature products as shown in Figure 1-4. New Products have fewer restrictions on common-

Fig. 1-4: ICR has been Proven in Product Design Stage

	NEW	VARIANT	EXISTING
Market	New	New/Expansion	Existing
NRE Investment	High	Med	Low
Commonality	Low	High	High
Tooling	None	Exists	Exists
Change from Baseline Design	Step	Step/Incremental	Incremental
Risk Tolerance	High/Med	Med	Low
Type of Supplier Design Involvement	Early Supplier Involvement		VA/VE

ality and allowance for "form, fit, or function" design changes. Existing products must fit an existing customer application and typically have tooling that is already "depreciated" and do not lend themselves to a "complete redesign." The cost required to upgrade existing applications in the field as well as modifying existing tooling or machines can be enormous. It's almost always easier to make cost reduction changes when a company can start with a "clean sheet of paper" than trying to modify existing designs.

In the following chapter we'll take a more detailed look at the five key tools involved in integrated cost reduction.

2

ICR'S FIVE KEY TOOLS OF CHANGE

EXECUTIVE SUMMARY: Integrated cost reduction (ICR) is an attempt to build an activity (cost reduction) into a working process. When it is fully implemented it can be used to spot, analyze, and take action on a broad menu of cost items.

The ICR initiative involves the development of a standardized and integrated set of analytical tools. The tools in ICR's toolbox are not new although the use of them in concert is relatively so. They include value analysis-value engineering, lean manufacturing, Six Sigma, supply chain management, and e-procurement. ICR offers a way to integrate each of these tools into a logical, effective strategy for cost reduction. Figure 2-1 graphically shows how the ICR Process merges these tools and operates within a cross-functional team environment.

In order to understand how ICR brings this integration about it is first necessary to fully grasp the basic principles behind each of the tools. The following chart is a condensed explanation of the dimension that each of the tools brings to ICR:

TOOL	DIMENSION
Lean manufacturing	Reduce cost cycle-time and waste in manufacturing
Six Sigma process	Homes in on cost of poor quality
Value analysis/value Engineering	Looks at costs imbedded in the design of each product
Supply chain management	Examines the supply chain itself for hidden costs
E-procurement	Uses power of internet to lower transaction costs and/or leverage volume

LEAN MANUFACTURING

The premise behind lean manufacturing is that waste in the production process is directly linked to time in the production process. Excess inventory, one of the most visible production wastes, is directly proportional to the leadtime in the production process. So, as the lead-time gets longer, the inventory gets larger. As lead time gets shorter, inventory gets smaller.

The Toyota production system, over the years, has become the most cited example of lean manufacturing. The Toyota production system attacks the seven forms of waste"MUDA"—excess inventory, over-production, wasted motion, transaction processing, queue time, rework, and transportation.

Companies that have implemented lean manufacturing successfully often follow a strategy that says, "Let's figure out a way to eliminate waste and reduce the cycle times in the production process." To do this there are many lean manufacturing sub-tools to choose from.

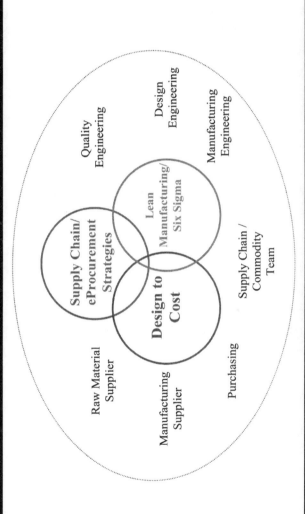

Fig. 2-1: Integrated Cost Reduction Process (ICRProcess)*

Merging Supply Chain/eProcurement, Lean, Six Sigma and VA/VE Strategies

*Note: The ICRProcess Materials are copyrighted and are being used by permission.

AS-IS PROCESS MAPPING

The first stage in the lean manufacturing inquiry process involves a set of process mapping exercises. A typical process mapping exercise might involve taking a particular assembly or component and step-by step articulating what goes on in the production process. Here, for instance, is a ten-step process map plan for production of a high-end gourmet cooking pot:

FIGURE 2-2: AS-IS PROCESS MAPPING

- **Step 1.** A sheet of metal is pulled out of the raw material storage stock.
- **Step 2.** The piece of sheet metal is sent to the shearing operation and half of it is cut off.
- **Step 3.** The sheared piece of sheet metal is taken to a blanking press operation where it is cut into a circular shape.
- **Step 4.** The circular shaped piece of metal is taken to a hydroform press where it is formed into the shape of a pot.
- **Step 5.** Rough edges of the pot are removed by hand finishing.
- **Step 6.** Pot is put into heat treating furnace to increase surface toughness.
- **Step 7.** Pot is sent to a cleaning and degreasing operation.
- **Step 8.** Chrome plating is applied to the pot to make it shiny and more attractive to customers.
- **Step 9.** Handle is attached to the pot.
- **Step 10.** Pot is cleaned one more time, packaged, and shipped to customers.

A real-life "as-is" map would also have all the additional steps that make up the "hidden factory" such as gathering lost tools, printing and sorting paperwork, shift-changeover, and downtime. The result of such step-by-step analysis of the production process is called an "as-is" or current state process map. In addition to doing the "as-is" process mapping, the lean manufacturing team may also look at "as-is" costs, the "as-is" inventory, and the "as-is" distances traveled.

In examining distance traveled through the factory, many companies literally take a pedometer, attach it to someone's leg, and physically walk the route that the pot would actually follow. What most companies find that do this is that there's an order of magnitude more time spent walking back and forth and in circles than in actually putting an item into production. Some lean manufacturing teams may also take stopwatches and measure the time between operations.

IDENTIFYING VALUE-ADDED PROCESS STEPS

Stage two in the lean manufacturing analysis process deals with value added. Most companies, as part of creating an "as is" process map (Figure 2-2) also do an analysis of their value added activities. Indeed, many companies that have implemented lean manufacturing have found almost the same statistic: Less than 10% of the time that a product is in the manufacturing cycle is actually involved in value added activities.

DEFINITION OF "VALUE-ADDED"

What is meant by value added activity? In simplified language, value added activity is defined by three necessary and sufficient items. All three of these conditions must be satisfied for a task to be considered value added:

(1) *The item is changed in some way.* Merely moving an item from one place in the plant to another does not qualify as a value adding activity. Eliminating non-value adding movements is a principle focus of lean.

(2) *The VA activity has to be one that the customer wants done and is willing to pay for.* Filling out paperwork or getting management approval signatures in most cases does not qualify as something the customer wants or something that the customer is willing to pay for. In short, it is a non-value adding activity.

(3) *A value added activity has to be done correctly the first time.* If the customer ordered a white pot and it was painted blue and has to be re-sprayed white, the overspraying does not qualify as a value added activity. It was not done correctly the first time. Instead of performing a value added activity, the maker of the pot has merely addressed a quality problem.

"TO-BE" OR FUTURE STATE PROCESS MAPPING

In the next stage of lean manufacturing analysis, a company creates a "to-be" or future state process map. The whole purpose of the "to-be" map is to find ways to eliminate as many of the non-value added activities in the manufacturing process as possible. Using the earlier pot example, in the current or "as-is" state there are 10 steps in producing the pot. In a "to-be" or future state process map such questions as these would be addressed: "How could we produce this pot using less time?" or "Is it possible to reduce cost by combining some operations?"

ACTION PLAN TO ACHIEVE FUTURE STATE

The final stage in the lean manufacturing process is execution of the "to-be" vision that will allow a company to eliminate from the process, cost, waste, and cycle-time. Executing an action plan to achieve this vision is the objective of lean manufacturing: You start out with an "as-is" process, estimate the amount of waste (time and distance that a product travels through the factory) in the manufacturing process, quantify how each step in the manufacturing process adds or fails to add value, and then develop a plan to change the manufacturing process in a way that will eliminate the manufacturing waste in the product. It takes time, effort and discipline to get from the "as-is" to the "to-be" states. Many internal "fief-doms" will justify their "non-value added" process steps as critical and cannot be eliminated.

THE SIX SIGMA PROCESS

There are three basic themes around which the Six Sigma process revolves. They are:

1. That prevention is better than inspection.
2. That variation is the source of most quality problems.
3. That variations that cause poor quality have a multiplied impact on a company's bottom lime.

Underscoring each of these themes is a universal theme that relates Six Sigma to integrated cost reduction: The cost of poor quality (COPQ) in a typical Two-Three Sigma manufacturing company in the U.S. runs between 20% and 30% of their sales. Despite these numbers, say many Six Sigma champions, most companies don't even know such costs exist.

What this means is that many companies aren't looking hard enough at the true facts. While they are struggling to eke out a 5% margin by typical cost cutting maneuvers, the cost of poor quality, which is often in the range of 20–30% of sales, is sitting out there with no one attacking it.

Some companies, however, are now coming to realize that the Six Sigma process is actually integral with lean manufacturing (aka "Lean Sigma"). This realization comes about despite the fact that the Six Sigma process was developed separately from lean manufacturing. (Motorola is credited with developing the Six Sigma program, but Toyota is generally considered the developer of lean manufacturing.

The point is that a growing number of companies that have been in the forefront of getting waste out of production are coming to champion the elimination of poor quality failures as part of the lean manufacturing process. Toyota, for instance, talks about the cost of product failures as waste in the production processs. It suggests that in order to go from 10% to 40% in cutting production costs, it's necessary to eliminate the quality defects.

Some lean manufacturing advocates have come down quite hard on companies that neglect product quality defects. They liken companies that have tried to do lean manufacturing without addressing their quality failures and defects to dogs chasing their own tails.

The problem, of course, is that product quality failures cannot be separated that easily from wastes in the production process. Lean manufacturing companies, for instance, are trying to take waste and time out of the production system. Those with JIT pull systems are trying to take waste out just in time. The crunch comes in such areas as safety stocks where there is no "just in case" inventories. So when they receive a defective part and have to send it back to the supplier they probably have to shut down the production line.

As a result the Six Sigma process is becoming a necessary

piece of the lean manufacturing process. An irony in the switch is that many in industry still look at processes like Six Sigma as essentially inspection procedures. They miss the point that Six Sigma practitioners almost universally preach that rather than focus on inspection to improve quality, companies need to focus on prevention using advanced statistical problem solving to improve quality. Many, indeed, point out that it has been scientifically proven that inspection, itself, is not a good tool for capturing failures. It has been proven that even a 100% inspection catches only about 80% of the defects.

Six Sigma, championed by Bob Galvin, the former CEO at Motorola, says that what is needed is a robust process to prevent defects from happening before they ever even occur.

The following analogy may help to explain how a typical Six Sigma process improvement actually happens. For instance, let's say that the yield from a particular four-axis machining process is less than 93% (approximately Three Sigma), while the processes in front and behind are operating above 99.4% (Four Sigma). The operator and manufacturing engineer who do NOT use Six Sigma methodology will typically employ the OFAT (one factor at a time) method and will change first the feed rate from .025in/sec to .015in/sec. When this does not solve the problem, they will speed up the spindle speed from 4000 rpm to 7000 rpm. Again the problem is not solved, so they experiment with a new cutting insert that the local manufacturing supply representative told them would double their yields for only a 25% price premium. Once again the problem persists, so they try to increase the coolant rate and simultaneously move the job to the more expensive five-axis machining center ($100/yr burden rate vs. $50/hr for the four-axis). We now have changed five factors and increased the cost of the suspect operation tremendously. Having exhausted all "manufacturing centric" ideas, the manufacturing engineer calls up his friend in engineering and requests the tolerances to be increased because "after we've tried everything, this part is just NOT producible with these outrageously tight specifications." The engineer begrudgingly agrees, the yield is now improved to 99% (3.5 Sigma), but nobody realizes until eighteen months later, when the part begins to fail prematurely on the customer's nickel, that the quality has been compromised.

After the OFAT method has increased the cost of the machining operation five ways and lowered the customer's performance, the Six Sigma "black belt" expert shows up with the following recommended approach. "Create a six multi-factor 'design-of-experiments'(DOE), which simultaneously tests various values of feed rate, spindle speed, cutter type, coolant flow, and machine type. In addition, the black-belt also finds out that there are two allowable material types on the drawing and adds these factors as well. Whereas the OFAT method would require dozens of 'experiments' to test six factors and would still not test every possible combination of factors, a DOE could be created to test all six AND the interaction effects in twelve to fifteen trials. The DOE would tell the exact contribution of each factor to solving the problem and heretofore unknown impact due to the interactions of two to three different factors at a time.

The real power of the Six Sigma methodology is eliminating the guess work required to solve the really thorny quality problems that plague many organizations. Furthermore, there are more than a dozen other quality improvement tools in the Six Sigma toolbox (besides DOE). Among them: measurement systems evaluation (MSE); paired-comparisons; Taguchi studies; root-cause analysis and corrective action (RCCA); statistical process control (SPC); and regression analysis.

How do companies implement Six Sigma? The typical methodology is to start with a Pareto analysis of the defective products. A Pareto is used to establish a hiearchy of product defects (worst problems, next worse, etc.), and is used to sort out problems from non-problems. Six Sigma methodology says to start with your biggest quality problems and then take those products and try to figure out the sources of variation in each product.

Using the example of the pot from the lean manufacturing segment, let's say it's supposed to hold three quarts. Using the ten steps talked about in lean manufacturing, let's key in on step 10, which is the final inspection. The inspector has a spec that says when three quarts are poured into the pot its contents should be 1/2 inch from the rim, so it doesn't boil over. The Second thing he looks at is the finish for scratches and blemishes. The third thing he does is look at the rim and runs a finger around the rim to make sure there are no sharp edges along the rim. Fourth thing he does is check the handle to make sure it's on tight.

Now, let's say the inspector takes a pot and pours three quarts of water into it and 1/2 quart runs out on the floor. The pot's too small! What happened? The inspector goes back to the operation where the pot was hydroformed. What he finds is the operator has a gauge that he uses to set the pressure in the press. Each time the operator puts a piece of metal into the hydroformer he adjusts the gauge. And depending on the weather or how the operator feels that day, he adjusts the gauge up or down.

Six Sigma would say that such a variation is evil and causing the problem. It would want to get to a point where a statistical study has been done and it has been proven exactly what the pressure should be set at to produce a perfect three quart pot every time. That may require performing an experiment that involves the use of such tools as design of experiments, paired comparisons, or root cause analysis.

Most of these tools are too specialized for examination here. Suffice to generally describe one of the most popular of the tools: design of experiments. The DOE practitioner would list all the different variables (eight in this case) that could result in the pot not holding three quarts. Among the variables are thickness of the metal, diameter of the blank, amount of oil used by the hydroform operator, pressure used, condition of the press itself, how much heat treating was done to the metal, temperature of the room, and cleanliness.

In design of experiments, each of the variables is tried out in conjunction with each other. Results of all experiments are fed into a regression analysis that gives the optimal setting to achieve a 3-quart pot every single time.

VALUE ANALYSIS/VALUE ENGINEERING

VA/VE uses a value equation that says that value to the customer is equal to function divided by cost. If you want to get more value you need to either increase the functionality at the same cost or decrease the cost at the same function. Either way the result is more value for the customer.

Originally called merely value analysis by its inventor, Larry Miles, an engineer in GE's purchasing operation at the end of World War II, VA/VE appears to have been the first attempt to deal with value objectively.

Stripped down to fundamentals, value analysis and value engineering involve the study of function. VA/VE looks at the relationships of design, function, method of manufacture, use of materials, and sources of supply. When conducted thoughtfully VA/VE seeks to answer this question: Does this product (proposed or now in use) meet all of the customer's requirements or can it perform better? Specifically, companies using value analysis techniques are seeking to quantify the true value of the goods and services that they buy and make.

Value analysis asks this question: In marketing this product, what are potential customers looking for and what are they willing to pay for these characteristics? What are the prized design characteristics in such areas as aesthetics, ease of use, portability, or wearability? As a cost reduction tool VA/VE is used to examine all the characteristics the targeted customer is looking in design. Goal: Elimination of features he/she is not willing to pay for.

As it first evolved value analysis was thought of as a tool for measuring the value performance of an item before it goes into initial production and after it has been manufactured for a period of time. Typically VA evaluation techniques were brought into play to detect whether:

- Unnecessary features had crept into the design during the manufacturing stage.
- A possible improvement had been left out of the design, or a less satisfactory one put in due to the lack of the right idea at the right time.
- Temporary conditions of supply or tooling had forced the company to use a less desirable material or less efficient method of processing.
- A design or production decision was the wrong one for the product.

As practitioners of VA saw it, in order to value analyze a specific item or service it is first necessary to identify their purpose. Over the years a methodology was developed that could be used in getting to the heart of value. Fundamentals needed to be uncovered by satisfactorily answering such questions as these:

- What is the function?
- How can the function be performed?
- What is the best way to do the job?

The primary function of an item can usually be defined in one or two words. For example, the primary function of a paper clip is to hold a number of pieces of paper in place. A vacuum cleaner is designed to "remove dirt" or "clean material."

Secondary functions also are involved. In the case of the paper clip the use function—holding the pieces of paper together—might be considered in conjunction with other considerations. Appearance, for example, may be important to the acceptance and salability of the paper clip. Perhaps the examination of the function needs to take into consideration the development of a new product that combines the functions of several desk products.

A more complex product like a vacuum cleaner has a number of secondary functions. It has to be able to store dirt. It also should be portable, easy to operate, shock resistant, and attractive.

The product as a whole has a prime function, but each component part can be described in terms of its specific task. One portion of the vacuum housing is made to hold the dust bag. Another section acts as a support for the motor. The motor drives a shaft. The cord transmits electricity. When you identify the function of each part, you almost automatically can suggest other ways of performing the same task.

Once function is defined, the next step is to determine how it can be performed. Since all value is relative, this step is best done by comparison. What else will do the job? How can the function be performed at the lowest overall cost consistent with the reliability required?

With a paper clip, there are a number of ways to perform the function. A paper weight might do the same job—a rock for that matter! Or a spring assembly might be more satisfactory for certain kinds of jobs. Perhaps the paper clip can be replaced by a staple. Different qualities of materials can be examined.

Comparison of different materials and methods of manufacture is what makes value analysis more than just getting lower unit costs. Value analysis requires determining how a function can be performed satisfactorily and economically.

Standard questions in most VA studies go like this: What other material will do the job? Can we use a standard part? Can assembly be simplified? Is the part necessary? Can we combine parts? Can delivery and storage of parts be made more efficient?

The next step, of course, is evaluation. The sequence goes like this:

- Gather all available information.
- Analyze the problem from all possible angles
- Evaluate all suggestions.
- Plan the re-design program.
- Carry it out.
- Record the results.

This sometimes is referred to as the blast, create, refine method. First, attack the problem from every conceivable viewpoint—blast. At this stage no idea is too far out, no suggestion is rejected.

In the second or creative stage suggestions are reviewed to see if there are alternate means of accomplishing the function. This produces a number of alternatives for action.

Finally, alternate approaches are refined and evaluated. The end result is the best combination of material, method, and cost to achieve the desired result.

From the start, to help identify the problem, the analyst asks these five basic questions:

- What is it?
- What does it do?
- What does it cost?
- What else will do the job?
- What does the alternative cost?

One point that needs to be made, however, is that if the value improvement proposed isn't function-oriented, then all that's being accomplished is some minor nibbling away at cost.

One of the things that helped to popularize VA/VE was that it was deceptively simple and easy to understand. It used plain talk to get at fundamental principles and then used simplified methodology to make value analysis unambiguous to its practitioners. When Miles first began preaching his theories of value analysis in the years after World War II, he laid out a set of ten principles for value analyzing a product or component. The principles go like this:

1. Does use contribute to value?
2. Is its cost proportionate to its usefulness?
3. Does it need all its features?
4. Is there anything better for the intended use?
5. Can a usable part be made by a lower-cost method?

6. Can a standard product be found that will be usable?
7. Is it made on proper tooling—considering quantities made?
8. Do materials, reasonable labor, overhead, and profit total its cost?
9. Will another dependable supplier provide it for less?
10. Is anyone buying it for less?

Over the years, the characteristics and use of VA/VE have been changing. From a production improvement tool it is being used more often as a product design tool—and for good reason. There are two different times in a product's life cycle when VA/VE can be successfully performed. The best time is during the design—before a product goes into production (see Figure 2-3). That's because typically 80% of product manufacturability cost is finalized once a product has been designed.

Once a product is in production, it's difficult to go back and start from scratch and change the design. Once the product is out in production there already is a big tooling bill, packaging has probably already been designed, and production floor space allocated.

Having made this point, however, there is a place for doing VA/VE after a product is in production. In cases where model design changes are few and far between many companies have been very successful in performing VA/VE on specific products. And there have been some companies that have been successful in applying VA/VE principles in both areas. (Chrysler's SCORE program is a good example of applying VA/VE principles to products while they are in production.) But, in general, the most successful application of VA/VE principles are most often being made at the design stage.

In recent years VA/VE has been assigned a major role in driving corporate global competitiveness—

Fig. 2-3: Benefits of Early Supplier Involvement in Design

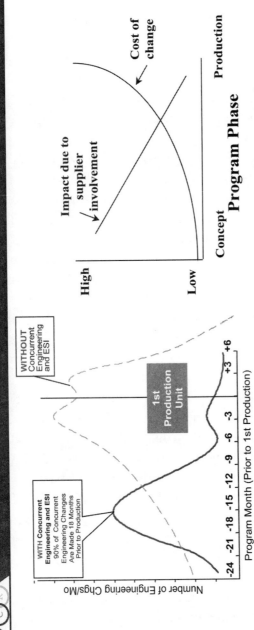

- Typically 80% of Product Cost and Ease of Manufacturability is designed in during development

- Many sourcing decisions are driven by near term needs (Prototype hardware delivery, unique of interesting technology) and do not address long term strategic requirements

- Changing from development to production sources just prior to production involves risk to schedule, quality, and cost

1. As a vehicle for spotting and eliminating excess costs from products and services without diminishing the value of those products and services.

2. As a major tool for implementing the very complex set of strategies surrounding integrated supply chain management—tools that would allow them to develop strategies along process lines without getting bogged down by traditional functional walls and silos.

SUPPLY CHAIN MANAGEMENT

Despite its importance as a tool for global integration of supply processes, our discussions on the use of supply chain management in ICR will seem perfunctory. We will not be looking at ICR from a global standpoint, but as a process focused on particular products that a company might manufacture. In that sense integrated supply chain management as we apply it in our ICR discussions, will seem more tactical than generally portrayed.

This shift in perspective is made for a reason. We wanted to demonstrate that a company does not need to do a complete redesign of its entire supply chain management system in order to implement the ICR process. Companies can implement an ICR program without first instituting vast organizational changes.

Nor are there any great demands on forcing a company to institute cross functional teaming. A company can be very traditionally organized around functional silos (e.g. engineering, finance, purchasing, etc.) and still use ICR. From an ICR standpoint we make no recommendations for companies to go out and redesign their entire supply chain management process. While we do in general recommend that all medium to large companies consider investing in the creation of integrated supply chains, this is not a necessary pre-condition to successfully implementing ICR. In fact, it is not necessary to have a fully deployed supply chain management and/or commodity team process to be successful at ICR, however—

- It IS necessary to have senior management support before ICR starts.
- It IS necessary to have technical experts of the products being worked (e.g. manufacturing engineering or design engineering).
- ICR IS focused on individual products, assemblies, or parts.
- ICR is NOT designed to achieve across-the-board productivity on ALL products simultaneously.
- ICR will NOT replace or compete with existing Six Sigma, lean manufacturing, or other re-engineering processes.

ICR works best in companies that are already experienced in these continuous improvement initiatives, but is more focused on one particular product, assembly, or component. Also, it's best applied to products that are already being targeted for some other continuous improvement initiative.

Instead, the center of our discussions of supply chain involvement in ICR will be on wastes for specific products in the supply chain. Where the first three tools concentrated on eliminating waste in the production cycle, the emphasis in supply chain management and e-procurement will be on wastes in the supply chain and logistics.

Typical questions that will be addressed in this area deal with such things as whether a company is handling specific product too many times, whether it is traveling back and forth across the country between suppliers too many times, whether such trips are necessary, whether a company is shipping five related parts in five different boxes. Instead of taking a global view of an entire company's supply chain process, our application of supply chain principles will be relatively restricted. The emphasis will be on trying to do a local optimization of a company's supply chain to eliminate the waste in its supply chain and logistics for specific product lines.

Having made this point, it is still important for an ICR implementor to have a succinct understanding of what supply chain management is about. Why? Because somewhere down the line success at ICR will call for greater integration and globalization of corporate processes. In addition, there are tremendous savings to be achieved for the ICR team by identifying specific wastes in the suppliers' "sub-tier" supply management process.

To begin with, supply chain management is a recognition of the direct link between control of the supply function and corporate competitiveness.

Some of the biggest opportunities for cost reduction are the result of "supplier rationalization," which in plain language is the reduction of the number of suppliers in a given commodity and leveraging the business into a smaller population of more qualified suppliers. Ultimately, dramatic cost reduction can occur by increasing the spend in the better quality and lower cost suppliers and decreasing purchases from less efficient suppliers. In addition, by increasing the spend with the company's preferred suppliers, these suppliers are said to be helped to spend/absorb their overhead better—which also is said to result in cost reduction. The good news about the concept of rationalization is that it is becoming widely understood by large companies. The bad news is that many of their suppliers are small to mid-size ($10–50 million/yr) companies that, by and large, have not taken advantage of the leverage that supplier rationalization provides. Some of the biggest savings opportunities available in ICR engagements occur by helping suppliers rationalize their own sub-tier suppliers.

No discussion of supply chain management would be complete without taking head-on the subject of second sourcing. We make the assumption that a company has already rationalized its supplier base before beginning ICR. We assume that a company has decided who its preferred and phase-out suppliers are and is actively transitioning business from a phase-out list to a preferred one. It makes absolutely NO sense to conduct ICR with a phase-out supplier. The action with a phase-out supplier is one-dimensional: MOVE THE BUSINESS TO A BETTER SUPPLIER AS SOON AS POSSIBLE! Conversely, old-school purchasing tactics of "lower your prices 5% or we'll move your parts," has NO PLACE in the discussion with preferred suppliers. ICR is designed for application with your preferred suppliers and will help them lower your prices 10-25% without moving parts. The preferred supplier wins with more business, your company wins with lower prices, and your customers win with better quality/delivery of your final products.

E-PROCUREMENT

In very plain terms, e-procurement is about leveraging the power of the Internet. It is an important tool in the ICR process because it provides overall balance to the process of examining costs and finding ways to reduce them. Where lean manufacturing, Six Sigma, and VA/VE deal mainly with the wastes involved in designing and making products, and supply chain management homes in on relationships with suppliers, e-procurement is a tool that focuses on the use of information to reduce costs.

Some of the most dramatic applications of Internet power can be seen among the larger original equipment makers (OEMs). Some, for instance, are setting up extranets on their web sites for suppliers to consult. There suppliers and potential suppliers can see the latest request for quotation (RFQ) complete with sets of technical specifications and blueprints and purchasing requirements.

At other companies buyers are using the Internet as a way to gather and store information on supplier performance. Such supplier performance evaluations can then be sent to other purchasing people or other departments in a company via the Internet. A growing number of companies are using the web to communicate customer demand to suppliers. In some cases procedures are being set up so that the demand data can be used in lieu of a formal purchase order—allowing the supplier to ship parts immediately.

All of this enhanced communication can result in significant cost reductions. One way that it achieves this is by effectively taking the buyer out of transaction processing—freeing him or her for more strategic duties. Internet relationships set up with key suppliers can be used by buying professionals to replace and often drastically reduce the many ancillary costs involved in making purchases.

As with supply chain management, companies transacting business with their suppliers in a traditional way may have difficulty in applying e-procurement tools strictly to ICR projects. Using the internet to send purchase orders or do electronic funds transfer after the parts are received, or to do bar coding, will find it difficult to do such things just for one product or product line. In these cases the best approach might involve looking into particular product lines for non-strategic or off-the-shelf items. ICR would recommend that the company look for a less expensive way to purchase them using reverse auctions, Internet buying, or EDI. Reverse auctions have their proper application in the purchase of non-strategic, off-the-shelf, or "true commodity" type items. Examples include fasteners, off-the-shelf supplies, consumables, and packaging materials. But a company should never attempt to use reverse auctions on strategic items (e.g. automotive transmissions, LCDs used in lap-top computers, jet engines for airlines, etc.).

In sum: While lean manufacturing, Six Sigma, and VA/VE are eliminating the waste in the production cycle, supply chain management and e-procurement are eliminating waste in the supply chain and logistics. Thus, while the first three tools are focused inside the internal manufacturing and assembly operations, the supply chain and e-procurement focus on the outside (how you transact business with the supplier). When hooked up in an ICR process the supply chain and e-procurement will be focused on waste. ICR will ask such questions as "where is the waste? Is it in transportation, logistics, transactions?, Are you sending POs to suppliers instead a long-term forecasts Is the supplier buying his parts strategically with long term contracts or PO to PO?"

3

OVERVIEW OF THE ICR PROCESS

EXECUTIVE SUMMARY: The concept for Integrated cost reduction is fairly straightforward. The essentials for implementing ICR are summarized in the process flow chart in Figure 3-0:

The ICR process flow begins with program engagement, during which top management signs on, and it ends with actual implementation of a comprehensive set of specific recommended actions. But in between winning executive management's endorsement and harvesting the savings are a number of steps or modules that absolutely need to be dealt with before there is an actual integrated cost reduction process. Within this five-part framework top management, suppliers, and product team participants need to be convinced about the need for a cost reduction program, educated about the areas that offer the most promising cost reduction targets, and won over to the adoption of ICR.

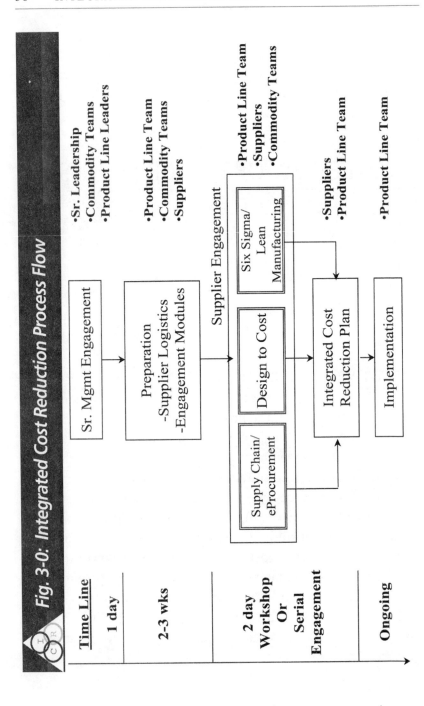

Fig. 3-0: Integrated Cost Reduction Process Flow

• • •

FIGURE 3-1 SUMMARIZES the objectives for each of the seven ICR engagements. Program engagement essentially involves selling the integrated cost reduction process to top management. If it's impossible to win backing for ICR at the top level in a company or strategic business unit, it's probably too soon to even consider ICR at this time. That's the bad news.

But the good news is that in many organizations top managers are already receptive—or at least attentive to the integrated cost reduction story. Many have already faced this situation: They just had a customer call them up and say, "Will you please lower your prices 20%." Or they, themselves, are the unhappy object of a reverse auction rather than being the customer of one. So when someone comes on the scene proposing a solution, that someone will in all probability have top management's wrapt attention.

Reverse auctions, themselves, require some comment here—mainly because they often represent the antithesis of ICR. Even though they have an enthusiastic, following among such industry giants as GE, United Technologies, and Hewlett Packard, they are often portrayed in very negative terms by suppliers. Typically they are portrayed by many suppliers as a necessary evil that is accepted by them out of desperation to keep their business with a customer.

Naysayers feel reverse auctions are mainly admired by customers who have reported large savings without really taking any true cost out of the product. In any case, reverse auctions have been in existence for only a few years and few companies have yet actually participated in them. Our guess is that as companies start to examine them more closely, reverse auctions

Fig. 3-1: Engagement Overview and Objectives

Sr. Mgmt Engagement	Face-to-face meeting to gain buy-in from Process owner
Preparation	2-4 wk process prior to supplier engagement
Supplier Engagement	1-2 day meeting with supplier's subject matter experts
Six-Sigma Engagement	Identify wastes due to cost-of-poor quality opportunities
Lean Manufacturing Engagement	Identify wastes due to inefficient manufacturing processes
Design-to-Cost Engagement	Identify wastes due to inefficient design practices
Supply-Chain/eProcurement Engagement	Identify wastes in the supply-chain and/or transactional processes

will be seen for what they are—an e-enabled form of win-lose, old school negotiations

Another factor favoring acceptance of the ICR message is the economic scene. Managers across the country will continue to scramble for economic advantage in the years ahead. Since more and more markets are going global every day, many companies see themselves working in a world of diminishing revenue expectations, growing customer demands, and tougher price competition.

IN SEARCH OF SILVER BULLETS

Ever since the late 1990s many companies have been looking to the Internet to see how it will help them gain economic advantage. Unfortunately, in many cases over-emphasis of the importance of e-business in the equation has distracted senior managers from making needed efforts in the direction of helping suppliers reduce costs through the use of such enablers as value analysis, lean manufacturing, and Six Sigma quality improvement efforts. This is an unfortunate diversion of attention, because, while the internet can save in the area of transaction costs, it's relatively superficial as a fundamental value proposition. It doesn't change the function of the product or the costs involved in producing the product.

Properly used, the internet can reduce transaction cost. But when thoroughly analyzed, transaction cost is really only a small piece of total cost. In the abstract it can look like a silver bullet, but e-business is often out of its element when significant cost reductions are under consideration.

Still, the appeal of silver bullets is often difficult to argue against and remains a serious impediment to winning commitment from senior management. In many companies senior managers are conditioned to want something easy. They were lured in the late '90s by promises of dot-com firms to sign up and watch profits increase. Unfortunately, even though the bubble burst in 2000–2001, some senior executives are still being sucked into the search for "simple solutions."

SHAPING THE ARGUMENT

In fairness, many (probably most) managers are under time constraints and need to be coaxed into investing the time and money required to launch a successful integrated cost reduction program. Senior managers are under extreme pressure so the arguments need to be cogent and forceful. And because time is such an important resource for most managers, the program used to explain ICR to senior managers needs to be limited to no more than a few hours in duration. That means that the person in charge of this module has to get across these items forcefully and in quick time:

- *A comprehensive plan for an integrated approach to cost reduction needs to be articulated.* Senior management needs a clear understanding of what ICR is about, how it will be implemented, resources needed, how it will require strong leadership and program management to be successful.
- *Program constraints need to be identified in fairly good detail.* Typically top managers will want to know about the cost of the program and budget demands. Such things as schedule and customer requirements will need to be spelled out in reasonably good detail and documented.
- *Program quality, cost, delivery, and service targets need to be thoroughly documented.* The evidence presented to back up these targets must be convincing.

- *Supplier engagement objectives and format need to be defined.* What will we expect of our suppliers and in what form will our supplier expectations be presented? Will we meet with suppliers one at a time, or in a conference setting with break-out sessions?
- *The best mix of cost reduction targets needs to be projected.* This calls for estimates of how much of proposed cost reductions will come from design to cost, from manufacturing, and from the use of supply chain management strategies and/or from the use of e-procurement tools.

PREPARATION

Without a doubt the most important module of the entire ICR process is the preparation. It's important to have all the data ahead of time, to identify what the costs are, and define opportunities before anyone sits down with a supplier or customer to talk about VA and VE.

Depending on how good a company's systems are, it usually takes two to four weeks to prepare for an ICR presentation. A great deal of time will be spent on pulling drawings and specifications and searching out relevant data about the products and the costs involved in their production.

Once the proper amount of preparation has been completed, it will be time for a two-day workshop or series of half day suppliers engagement. The program is highly concentrated and is usually presented in these three modules:

- Design to cost. This module probably bears the most resemblance to traditional value analysis/value engineering programs (e.g. Chrysler's "SCORE" program).
- Manufacturing.This module closely resembles traditional

lean manufacturing and Six Sigma projects (e.g. GE's "Kaisen" blitz).

- Supply chain/e-procurement. This module is devoted to logistics, supply chain management, and strategic sourcing and e-procurement improvements subjects.

Each of the modules is attended by integrated product teams (IPTs), suppliers, and supply chain representatives. Each module is kicked off with an explanation of how the process is expected to work. Each module also features a listing and explanation of results that might be anticipated in the ICR review.

Typical expected results for the supply chain/e-procurement module include:

- Discussion of aftermarket issues such as repair and overhaul and spares.
- Definition of supplier cost sharing expectations.
- Explanation of make/buy and outsourcing opportunities (including variations on current outsourcing themes), where supplier may supply higher-level assemblies made from components they already provide.
- Development of an understanding of the benefits of long term contracting.
- Development of a full understanding of the benefits of volume leveraging by part family to reduce supplier overhead and component cost.
- Understanding of potentials of procurement from lower costs or global sources.
- Review of packaging alternatives (e.g. kitting).

For the design to cost module some of the important areas that get tapped in searching for expected results include:

- Material and special processing alternatives.
- Standard parts/components/specifications used.
- Elimination of non-value added design and/or testing requirements.
- Development of designs consistent with benchmark manufacturing processes and suppliers developed—using new technology and design optimized for the manufacturing process.
- Expansion of lessons learned to other strategic business unit products.

Areas in the manufacturing process module offering good potential for significant results:

- Streamlining of process for reduced cycle times and cost. This includes elimination of non-value activity at supplier; exploitation of synchronous manufacturing strategies; elimination of redundant testing and inspection; elimination of scrap, rework, and other cost of quality elements.
- Focusing of manufacturing technology on product applications. This includes evaluation of alternative manufacturing processes and utilization of benchmark manufacturing centers/suppliers.
- Lessons learned and expanded to other strategic business units in the company.

Once general procedures and expectations are reviewed, teams are formed and team leaders assigned. Each team breaks off into a separate meeting. Engineers meet with engineers and talk about VA and VE. Manufacturing people meet with manufacturing people. Quality people meet with manufacturing

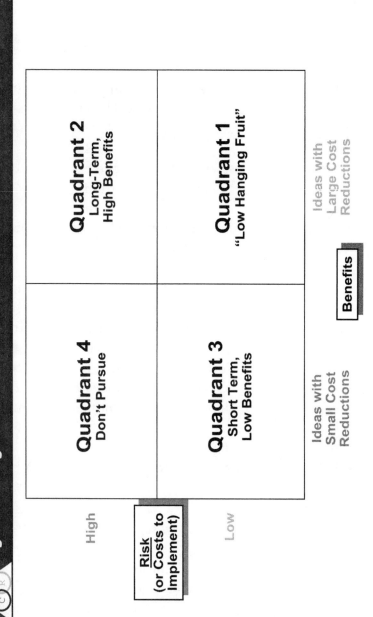

Fig. 3-2: Using the 2x2 Matrix to estimate the risks vs. benefits

people about waste and lean manufacturing. Business people and procurement people meet together.

At the end of the two days (this can be longer or shorter depending on product complexity) the teams are brought back together and each module reports on what it came up with. The design to cost team identifies, for example, 27 ideas; manufacturing 15; supply chain/e-business 20. Then the individual lists are consolidated into one master list. From the master list a list of the top 10, or 20, or 25 (depending on resources) is selected. These are the ideas calculated to yield the biggest bang for the buck. ICR uses a simple, but very powerful tool, the "2 x 2 Matrix" (see Figure 3-2) to focus priority on the right projects.

From the list an integrated cost reduction plan is formed and implemented. At this point the enterprise begins to make sense. It's like many problem-solving company undertakings. There's a list of things to be done. People are assigned to do these things and a time line of about how long it will take them to do it. There is a schedule and a list of action items that need to be completed with preliminary due dates.

Once launched, the process is ongoing, because, depending on how many ideas you have, investigative projects have a way of generating new and better ideas. The main limitation for most companies is the resources available and the commitment of the people assigned to the ICR teams.

ICR PROCESS EXECUTION STEPS FOR PRACTITIONERS AND PROJECT MANAGERS

ENGAGING SENIOR MANAGEMENT—
THE FIRST CRITICAL STEP

EXECUTIVE SUMMARY: The first step in setting up an ICR project is winning senior management approval and backing. In granting its okay and backing senior management will want a comprehensive idea of what's involved. This will require the engagement of the senior manager(s) and the ICR project leader in which very key pieces of information will need to be transferred. A diagram of this data transfer looks like this:

KEY ISSUES

For senior managers	For project leader
ICR's strategic plan	Management approval, backing
Projected payoff	Management's expectations
Estimated costs	Project budget
Level of risk involved	Acceptable risk for each change
Results timeline	Deadline for completion

One point has to be clear throughout the thinking that goes into any ICR project: There can be no success without a full buy-in of senior management. Senior management engagement is not just important—it's critical.

Senior management ultimately takes blame or credit for all profit improvement initiatives. Therefore, how well ICR is presented to top management, will determine how well the concept and its implementation will be accepted and promoted within the organization.

• • •

I N MOST CASES senior management engagement is a two-part process. The first part is a general explanation of what is proposed, the objectives, and how we intend to get there. Simply put, it's a sales pitch for an ambitious undertaking. The second part (assuming the senior management agrees to examine ICR further) is a detailed look at the current situation and a documentation of key cost targets and a detailed explanation of criteria to be used for identifying cost targets as well as identifying the targeted suppliers.

"WHY WE WON'T FAIL THIS TIME"

At the outset, executive management in many companies will want a thorough explanation of the performance of any past profit improvement efforts. If there have been failures or partial failures they will want to know why they happened and what assurances there are that ICR will not end in disappointment. (One help in answering these questions can be found in the four case studies in the Appendix. These will explain how the process has worked at *Fortune 100* companies in the past and how it might be applied at your firm.)

In any case, it's practically a given that presenters in the senior management engagement will be challenged to explain why so many continuous improvement initiatives fail on their own and why so many companies fail to achieve the expected improvement in their profit margins as the result of implementing initiatives such as total quality management (TQM), Hoshin planning, statistical process control, and dozens more others over the past four decades.

The answer(s) will require both tact and a level of frankness some top managers may not initially appreciate. That's because in many (maybe most) cases a large part of the answer is that past efforts were not enterprise-wide in application. In fact, it will probably turn out that most of the failures were the result of initiatives being run as stand-alone pillars.

In blunt terms, a big reason for many past failures has to be chalked up to failures of senior management. Often senior managers simply aren't very good at understanding organizational complexity. Many who have been chosen for their financial or marketing skills, for instance, find themselves looking for simple solutions to complex operations problems that they don't fully understand. What's more, many of these complex problems cross over functional boundaries, time boundaries, geographic boundaries. They last months, sometimes years, and many senior managers continue to be ill-prepared to handle them. Complicating the situation further, many continuous improvement initiatives, themselves, often fail to take into account the complexity of the businesses in which they're employed. Simply put, many senior managers are responsible for these failures by virtue of (1) their failing to understand organizational complexities, (2) their focusing of efforts on achieving simple solutions, and/or (3) an over-reliance on consultants, who are typically very bright and well educated, but lacking in "real-world" experience.

AVOIDING THE TRAIL OF "UNSUCCESS"

Often, too, there is a trail of "unsuccess" that starts at the top and seeps through the company—people who are assigned to head up new initiatives are lacking the operations experience and breadth needed to make corrections. For a re-engineering project implementation to be successful requires experience in budgets, human resources, technical constraints, project management, and all kinds of conflicting organizational/executive agendas that they are unprepared to address. In such cases the fault lies in a general lack of appreciation that most of the initiatives being tried are too complex for the skills of those who are asked to take them on.

These and other related failings need to be dealt with right at the beginning of senior management engagement. Senior managers need to understand from the beginning that ICR is an enterprise-wide approach to cost reduction—not a consulting exercise introduced from the outside. And speaking of consultants, this typical scene especially needs to be avoided: A consultant visits with the president of a company or general manager of a strategic business unit and says, "I want to improve your quality, by implementing a Six Sigma process." The president then brings in the VP in charge of quality and says, "I have a consultant I want you to talk to in order to fix our quality problems."

Unfortunately consultants often deserve a large portion of blame for past failures of profit improvement programs. Senior managers without a clear understanding of the problems that need to be dealt with, bring in "experts" to give them plans and outlines of what needs to be done. Sadly, most consultants who get called in to help have little real world experience and rely mostly on theoretical experience. When they reach the implementation stage with their theories on such things as strategic sourcing, lean manufacturing, and Six Sigma, they often run into significant problems not covered on a textbook level.

Such typical scenes surface every day in manufacturing where the consultant promises to lower inventory, improve manufacturing processes, and streamline supply chain and other processes. In all of these areas senior management needs to recognize that costs are not strictly the responsibility of manufacturing, quality, design, business management, or purchasing. Unfortunately, in many cases neither senior management groups nor the consultants they hire have a clue about which "organization" or business processes are the primary drivers of costs.

The answer is: All of the functional areas just cited own a piece of the cost problem. When the general manager of a strategic business unit is being beaten up by the CEO for not making his/her numbers, the GM can't say, "It's the VP of manufacturing's problem and I replaced him/her and now my cost problem will be solved." In essence, this top manager is taking the silver bullet approach and turning it into a human resources problem—without actually solving the real problem.

Top managers also need to have it impressed on them that it is very easy to trivialize ICR into being looked upon as "another of those business fads." Because most manufacturing companies already are using at least one of ICR's tools, the temptation is to say "we're already doing that!" While it isn't necessary to start from scratch with lean manufacturing, Six Sigma, supply chain management, or VA/VE, it's important for senior managers to recognize that ICR is a vehicle they can use to pick those things they're already doing and integrate them under a more strategic framework. ICR gives management a more methodical, enterprise-wide focus to cost control.

WHAT EVERYONE NEEDS TO UNDERSTAND

Fundamentally there are three absolutes that need to be driven home to senior management. Without exception, every senior manager needs to understand that:

1. The senior manager in the enterprise must champion the process. This is a responsibility that can't be delegated, and unless it is fully accepted the ICR initiative will never get off the ground.
2. The project will be competing for resources with other continuous improvement initiatives that are already going on. Provision will need to be made in many instances for integrating "pre-existing" initiatives into the overall ICR strategy.
3. Case studies indicate that ICR projects typically achieve 50-100% ROI within twelve months. Nevertheless, ICR will require an investment in money and resources. In most cases expenditures will be in direct proportion to potential payoff.

OBJECTIVES

What do those presenting an ICR initiative need to walk away with from a senior management engagement? First thing they need is a strategic plan for the ICR process. That means they need to know how long they have to achieve results and a statement of objectives. They also need enough details to move to the next step in getting resources and setting budgets.

Another essential is an understanding of what are some of the key constraints that the business is living with. For instance, they need an understanding of how customer requirements will affect the budget and staffing. More subtly, when the top executive says it's impossible to devote any people or money to the initiative, the presenter needs to determine whether that spells the end of ICR permanently or temporarily.

Those heading the ICR push also need to get some specific business targets identified by senior management. For instance: What are the "real" problems from a cost and profitability standpoint? Which product lines are affected? What is the size of the major cost problems? The presenter(s) also needs to find out how broad the major problems are and whether problems affect just one product and one customer, or extend across many products. Are the resources required proportional to the size of the problem? Answers to these questions help in scoping the rest of the ICR process.

Engagement with senior management should also result in establishing specific supplier objectives. If there's a small problem with one small product, can it be handled with one engineer? Is there a need for a complete ICR team? How many suppliers will be involved and for how long?

Assuming that senior management is aware of the very palpable risks as well as the potential payoffs, one thing that it will want to know about right off is what to expect. What are the potential payoffs? What are the risks? What are the costs? Specifically what senior management expects out of this program management effort is acomprehensive plan outlining an integrated approach to cost reduction for the business units or just one product line.

A significant part of this presentation will deal with what customers are facing and what they expect. For instance, do they have goals to achieve a "step-function" reduction in costs by, say, 25%, or 10%, or 5%? And if they do, what is the time line they're working with? Supplier engagement objectives and format need to be defined clearly in the presentation. And depending on how much time is available to achieve results, the approach will be anything from a slow measured development to a big bang.

FIGURE 4-1:
DELIVERABLES FROM THE
SENIOR MANAGEMENT ENGAGEMENT

- Total market potential of current and potential future products (how many more will we ship? How many more years is this product good for?)
- Customer flow down requirements.
- Program requirements.
- Current cost baseline of the product.
- Goals for the new cost of the product.
- Cost reduction objectives. (What's the best mix of business, design, and manufacturing opportunities estimated. What percent of the cost reduction will come from design, manufacturing, procurement?)
- Supplier engagement format. How do we plan to do this—in a single meeting with all suppliers, in a series of meetings over a period of time?
- Criterion to be used to prioritize ideas and proposals.

SENIOR MANAGEMENT ENGAGEMENT DELIVERABLES

To lay the foundation for a successful ICR program, there are a number of issues that will need to be carefully agreed to with senior management. These issues (summarized in Figure 4-1) will each need to be discussed, clarified, and defined with senior management before beginning the ICR process.

- *Total market potential* (current as well as future products). The objective is to identify total market potential and customer demand for the targeted product(s). Key deliverables are potential annual and total production volumes and additional business potential related to the base program.

Why is this important? Cost reduction potential, as well as the financial commitment to accomplish it, is predicated on future production demand rates. A product in the last one to two years of its lifecycle is not a good candidate for ICR. It will be difficult to amortize the investment over dwindling production rates. Dwindling customer demand is typically a signal that production-line needs to be refreshed—or replaced with newer technology. ICR can help here too, but the ICR process is conducted differently for a new product than an existing one. (Case study #4 describes the process for a new product.)

- *Program and customer requirements*. Objectives are documentation of enterprise or program requirements. Key deliverables include key strategic business issues; after-market business issues (e.g. spares, repair and overhaul, maintenance); customer requirements in terms of product performance, quality, cost, schedule, warranty, offset (e.g. local content, joint venture); resource availability; acceptable level of risk, budget, schedule, development, and hardware procurement.

Why is this important? Flow-down of customer requirements is critical to creating value as well as reducing costs. Often an end-item "OEM" interprets its customer's requirements on behalf of its suppliers. Experience has shown that when the suppliers are exposed to the actual requirements of their customers' the supplier can often find innovative, more cost effective methods of achieving the end-customer's real objectives. Furthermore, it is necessary to have a clear picture of the program's overall objectives and constraints before beginning the ICR program. Making an ICR plan that involves twelve people and ten months of effort makes little sense to a program that has only a budget for three people for six months.

- *Current product cost baseline.* Objective is to document baseline cost. Key deliverables: Pareto of product cost elements.

Why is this important? Knowing where the current product cost is set at establishes the baseline to work from. A "Pareto" analysis of the cost drivers (highest to lowest cost elements) identifies the first opportunities to attack cost first.

- *New product cost targets for major cost elements.* Objective is to document cost targets for major cost elements. Key deliverables are establishment of cost reduction goals to achieve product target cost.

Why is this important? Very few companies have a clear understanding at the beginning of an ICR project where the biggest cost reduction opportunities will be found. Therefore, common practice is to "allocate" the cost reduction objectives according to the value of each sub-assembly or component.

For example, if a 25% overall cost reduction goal is set and the powerplant accounts for 15% of the total vehicle cost, then the goal could be somewhat unscientifically set to reduce the entire power-plant price by 25%. A 25% reduction on 15% of the total product yields 3.75% total product cost savings (.25 x 15% = 3.75%). Therefore, if the power-plant ICR team achieves its objectives, that leaves 21.25% worth of cost reductions still unaccounted for (25% - 3.75% = 21.25%). However, it could be decided that the power-plant is ripe for cost reduction and should bear a greater burden of the total product cost (e.g. 35% x 15% = 5.25% total vehicle reduction).

- *Cost reduction strategy*. Objective is to estimate the "best mix" of opportunities that will achieve the overall cost reduction goal. Key deliverables include anticipated cost reduction mix for the three ICR modules (business/ procurement, design to cost, and manufacturing/process) plus the overall cost reduction goal.

Why is this important? Depending on the program constraints, it may be easier to achieve savings in various areas. If a program is operating under a government contract or other high technology environment, design changes may be discouraged by the end customer (INTEL, for example, has a "copy exact" policy with its suppliers.). It may be necessary to achieve most or all of the cost reductions via the manufacturing and supply chain modules. Conversely, if a product has very little supplier content and has a high-value added content (such as shoes or assembled toys), then it may be desirable to target savings from design or manufacturing changes. Finally, in an environment where a product is highly regulated for safety concerns, then any changes to the design or manufacturing process may be discouraged by the FAA, FDA, or DOE. In this case, supply-chain and e-procurement savings may account for 90% of the total opportunity.

- *Supplier engagement format.* Objective: to define supplier engagement format, schedule, and assign responsibilities to implement the ICR process. Key deliverables include a defined engagement format (supply workshop or individual engagements), ICR implementation team identified; tentative schedule defined; boundary conditions and direction to ICR team defined.

The supplier engagement format is critical to pulling off a professional project. Making sure that all attendees are aware of the agenda, deliverables and process for the engagement meetings will save valuable time and confusion on "the day." Since many participants will be flying in from other parts of the country or globe, it is important to have an effective and efficiently run meeting.

- *Cost reduction feasibility ranking.* Objective: Development of feasibility ranking matrix used to summarize and prioritize ideas generated during the supplier engagement modules. Deliverables include definition of major decision criterion and definition of criterion weighting factors. Tools: example of feasibility ranking matrix, blank feasibility ranking matrix, explanation of feasibility ranking.

Experience has shown far too often that a feasibility rank-ing is not done before a project starts. Normally a team will brainstorm first and then present its recommendations to se-nior management for concurrence. Many team leaders are then disappointed to have their ideas rejected as having too high schedule, weight, or reliability impact to be implemented on this particular product. By having senior management assign "weighting factors" ahead of time, the ICR team can make the appropriate trade-offs ahead of time. For example, many automakers in their efforts to achieve government mandated "CAFE" standards (corporate average fuel economy) have deemed that "one pound of weight is equal to $X per vehicle, etc. Similarly, a Y% improvement in reliability = a 25% reduc-tion in warranty cost = $Z/vehicle in cost savings.

NEED FOR UNDERSTANDABLE METRICS

One major obstacle to successful senior management engage-ment is that executive management often doesn't understand the metrics that are used to measure performance in such areas as sourcing, manufacturing, and procurement. These are middle management metrics and bear little resemblance to those used to ensure the effectiveness of senior management. While senior managers are judged by such metrics as profitability and invento-ry, middle managers have to answer for cycle time performance, productivity, and defects. Making sure that executive managers understand the significance of such measures is an important job for ICR project leaders.

One common measurement link that is beginning to be understood at all levels in many companies, however, is cost of poor quality. Cost of poor quality is a financial metric. It's a measurement of the lost profit as the result of waste. It's a negative value adder. And it goes well beyond scrap, re-work, and warranty that most companies measure—to include far more important elements such as customer returns and potential lost sales due to poor quality.

ICR project leaders would do well to present their metrics about ICR in relation to cost of poor quality where appropriate. Indeed, more than one study has pointed out that in the average U.S. company the cost of poor quality runs in the neighborhood of 15-25% of revenue.

SENIOR MANAGEMENT PREROGATIVES

Finally, it's important to recognize that there are two general categories of ICR cost reduction projects: (1) ICR projects on products during the initial design and pre-production phase and (2) cost reduction on products that have already been designed and need to be produced less expensively. Each type of project is handled differently. On a new product, the three modules are inseparable—changes to the initial design will dramatically affect manufacturing and supply chain, etc. If it's an existing product there's a choice of going to all three modules—the supply chain, design to cost, and manufacturing—or only one or two.

When meeting with senior management, part of the constraint it will lay out is likely to be that this is a new product and needs to be introduced by June of next year. Or you have six months to complete this project. Or that this is an existing product that we're losing money on and "a major customer just told me to lower my price 5% more." The point: Decisions in many of the areas just examined are senior management decisions. Therefore, if the ICR project leader doesn't start out by seeking and winning approval at the senior management level, he/she is just spinning wheels.

GETTING DOWN TO SPECIFICS

Part 2 of senior management engagement gets down to the nuts and bolts of ICR. During this part of the discussion a data sheet (see *www.icrprocess.com* for access to the data sheets) is actually filled out with the senior manager. It serves as a summary sheet for future analysis. On it, the manager provides overview information about the program. For example:

- Under the opportunity section information is filled in about anticipated yearly production, aftermarket potential, and follow-on business.
- The schedule section answers such questions as: When will the program start? Will the design be frozen? When will mature production start?
- The requirements section deals with cost, reliability weight, joint ventures, terms and conditions, prior terms and conditions that affect ability in this program engagement.
- Customer objectives if there are any, deal with acceptable levels of risk and resources—How many people? How much time? How many dollars?
- The next stage involves breaking the product down into its logical parts—What's the cost? What's the target cost? What is its cost today? What's your objective for the cost? Could we substitute target reliability for cost, target weight, or durability?

At the end of the check list are items requiring senior management commitment: "These are the things I want the senior managers to commit to." This checklist is followed by a listing of participants—the team that will be assigned to the project (names of team members, manufacturers, supply chain management, phone numbers). When the ICR project leader meets with the senior manager(s), the whole check list needs to be filled out.

FEASIBILITY RANKING

The final step in the top management engagement module is the creation of a feasibility ranking.

Top management is asked to take part in the ranking process and selection of the best projects for the company. In some cases top management will say, "If we can save 30% of the cost, that's worth a five to me because that's my goal. If I can save less than 5%, that's only a 1." Some top managers will be willing to take more or less risk than others. If a brand new design is involved, they may be willing to tolerate a high risk. If it's an old design there may be little or no risk tolerance.

This ranking exercise is meant to give a general idea of the thinking that goes into setting feasibility rankings. Each business using the ranking system can tailor this to whatever its issues are or the business in which it is operating.

The intent of this part of the engagement is to give top management some sound information on which they can determine how much risk they are willing to tolerate in pursuing cost reduction. It's a time for the CEO to probe just what a 5 is; for the project leader to size up the CEO's opinion. It's an opportunity for the project leader to learn about non-negotiable positions and the worst risk senior management is willing to tolerate.

These feasibility metrics will be used to prioritize all the ideas generated during the various engagement modules. Project leaders sit down with managers, designers, manufacturing engineers, procurement managers shaping the outlines of their proposals for each module. Managers develop a time line and risk and feasibility ranking. The ranking sheet (see www.icrprocess.com) scores savings potential, risk, cost to implement, time to implement, quality, and weight. Each is ranked on a scale of one to five (5 is good, 1 is bad). Rankings are totaled and the list of proposed projects is presented to top management. Those proposals that rank highest are presumed to be the ones with the most promise.

5

PREPARATION

EXECUTIVE SUMMARY: Assuming executive buy-in has occurred, preparation becomes the most important success criteria in the integrated cost reduction process. In fact, we would estimate that 90% of the results possible from an ICR initiative are enabled at the preparation stage. In addition, one of the main reasons that ICR can be done so quickly and economically is the fact that a great deal of the required planning takes place before the supplier engagement meetings actually take place.

The checklist that follows is a good outline of the data that needs to be gathered in preparing for an ICR launch. It helps to summarize in fairly good detail the activities, responsibilities, and crunch dates that will come up in the preparation stage. If a company has robust IT, engineering, and financial systems, these items may be completed in two to three weeks. If extensive manual data extraction is required, you can double or triple this estimate.

PREPARATION FOR ENGAGEMENT

	Activity Team *

1. Baseline sourcing analysis. .... ICR
    - Current cost
    - Target cost
    - Variance to target
    - Totals for current suppliers
    - High dollar raw materials by supplier
2. Review of existing make/buy policies .... ICR
3. Select and prioritize suppliers to engage..................... ICR
4. Part grouping and sourcing optimization................... ICR
    - Parts eligible for second sourcing
    - Convert make to buy (outsource candidates)
    - Unique parts
5, Define program strategy to engage suppliers .... ICR
6. Designate teams to implement ICR process .... ICR
    - Purchasing
    - Engineering
    - Operations
    - Commodity team
7. Teams organize, establish tactical plan, complete check-
    lists, assemble data........SE
8. ICR engagement session logistics............................... SE
9. Notify suppliers.. SE
    - Objective
    - Agenda
    - Supplier preparation requirements
    - Documentation requirements

* ICR=ICR core team, SE=Supplier engagement teams (may be specific to each supplier/commodity)

• • •

ONCE SENIOR MANAGEMENT has said, "Here are our problems"—i.e. the market demands that we lower prices on
these items by 5%—there is a starting place. You start asking,
"Where are all the costs in these products?" Indeed, much time
is spent in the preparation stage on hypothesis—on identifying
costs and identifying opportunities. Those with experience in
ICR initiatives point out that once an understanding of what
the problems are, solutions start to show their faces. Once the
ICR team has figured out where all the costs are, then it becomes obvious where it will want to focus its attention—i.e.
manufacturing, supply chain, quality, and design.

PLANNING FOR ENGAGEMENT

The focus in the preparation module is on supplier selection
and action planning for ICR. Major participants in the preparation process are the integrated product team (IPT), supply
chain managers, and suppliers.

The objective of the preparation module is summarized by
these five items:

- Optimization of the mix of products, assemblies, or com-
  ponents targeted for cost reduction.
- Selection of appropriate suppliers to be be engaged in the
  ICR process.
- Identification of ICR teams for each supplier engagement.
- Development of supplier engagement tactical and logisti-
  cal plans.
- Organization of business and technical information or
  data to support the three main supplier engagement mod-

ules—manufacturing process, design to cost, and supply chain/e-procurement.

In the executive summary at the beginning of this chapter we have listed the steps that can be used as a cookbook summary of what needs to be done in preparing for an ICR project. A detailed checklist can be found on *www.icrprocess.com*.

The data assembled in the preparation stage is used to support the above objectives. In physical terms data collection involves such things as pulling drawings, locating specification data about products and components, collecting product histories, and getting cost breakdowns of the products or product lines that will be under study. Gathering this data is considered by many to be the single most important aspect of the preparation. Depending on how good a company's systems are and how complex its cost analysis is going to be, preparation usually takes between two and four weeks to complete.

Among the data that are collected in the preparation module for the targeted products:

- **Product histories.** Included in this category are product cost trends for the past year or two—asking such questions as: What's been happening to these costs? Have prices for them been going up or down? If they've been dropping, that could be an indicator that a lot of cost has already been taken out in that areas and it may not be a good area of opportunity for a cost reduction inquiry.
- **Purchased component data.** This information can be highly valuable in the ICR process inquiry. In many cases prices on every single component that goes into an assembly will need to be looked at for clues to potential cost reduction. Another area of important information is

a listing of the suppliers for each component that goes into an assembly. Automated bill-of-material downloads to a spreadsheet, then sorted by highest value components and/or suppliers, is most beneficial.

- **Quality data.** Quality rejection history is especially helpful in focusing on where cost pressures are. Many companies tend to ignore the cost of poor quality as a major factor in cost reduction. Many tend to view product rejects as an operator error or machine tool problem. Often they ignore the possibility that the fault lies in the product design or the selected manufacturing process. Often they completely ignore the obvious solution of redesigning a product or a component to make it more manufacturable to eliminate quality rejections and the costs that accompany them.

- **Manufacturing and assembly instructions.** Also to be collected are copies of all the manufacturing and next higher assembly instructions. Often they can be a great eye opener to the supplier who probably has never seen them. They can hold insights into ways of reducing or cutting costs. Where possible, copies of this data should be sent to the supplier a week ahead of time.

Often times, information collected for engagement on one product is useful in mapping cost reduction analysis on related products. A typical example of how this comes about: In digging out the data needed on one product, the purchasing history indicates that similar material specifications are used for four other products also under study, and are produced by five different suppliers. Knowing this fact can help to shape the direction of future inquiry—from a focus that was largely on design and manufacturability to one mainly concerned with supply chain and e-procurement considerations. The problem now becomes: There are five different products at five different suppliers that are costing far too much money. The solution: Put all five products together with one supplier and leverage the volume.

COST DATA

Some of the cost material needed will be available directly from accounting. Much, however, will not be readily available and must be searched out. That's because much of the cost breakdown material needed in the ICR process is radically different from the costs tracked in other parts of the company by accountants busy tracking the company's business health.

While corporate accountants readily involve themselves with labor, overhead, and materials costs, their breakdowns are usually too crude for the ICR process. For ICR purposes cost information has to be broken down more finely. For instance, if it's at all possible to tell how much an individual product feature costs, that information can be highly significant and useful in the type of cost analysis performed in ICR. Unfortunately most corporate accounting and financial departments don't get involved with cost data that is tuned to such a detailed level.

Manufacturing and design engineers often can look at an assembly line and know at each assembly line stop, how many parts go into that station or work cell. And they can tell you the cost of those parts that go into the work cell. Still, even for them, it's very difficult for anyone to determine how much labor it will take to install a certain component versus how much labor it takes to install another component that is designed differently.

In looking at two different components on two different vehicles, both may price out the same, but because one is installed one way and the other another way, they cost out completely differently. Installation costs may be radically different for two components that look the same. As a result, most companies have a hard time coming up with these cost data.

PREPARING ADMINISTRATIVELY

How many suppliers will it be necessary to meet with? How much time should be spent with suppliers—how much with each supplier? Are we going to spend two hours with each supplier per day or will we bring five suppliers in over a course of three days? Or, do we do it all at once? Another important administrative question involves where the engagement process will take place. Where are you going to meet with them—at your location or at the suppliers' location? The way the decision is usually made is to go back to the preparation work and determine where the greatest opportunities lie.

If you believe your biggest area of opportunity is in the design, then it is probably a good idea to have your suppliers come to where your engineers are to talk about design changes. If opportunities appear to lie in lean manufacturing and quality, you may want to go to the supplier's factory.

The preparation process is necessarily shaped by the workshop or serial engagement that is to follow. Engagement can be conducted in a number of different ways. The process described here is called supplier engagement. It's designed to do the cost reduction process quickly meeting face-to-face with the suppliers and conducting the supplier engagement over a two day period. The engagement is very concentrated and allows for going through all three supplier engagement modules—design to cost (VA/VE), manufacturing (lean manufacturing and Six Sigma), and the supply chain/e-procurement module (involving mainly logistics and supply chain management).

All three module meetings can be conducted in parallel. The day is opened with an explanation to suppliers how the process will work. The exact same charts are used for each supplier engagement and then team leaders are assigned and the general meeting is broken out into three separate meetings. Engineers meet with engineers and talk about VA/VE. Manufacturing people meet with manufacturing people. Quality people meet with manufacturing people about waste and lean manufacturing. Supply chain and e-procurement people meet together.

At the end of two days the participants are all brought back together in a combined meeting. At this meeting, module team leaders present a summary of the best ideas developed in each module. All the ideas are combined into one master list. From the master list the top twenty ideas across all of the processes are selected. The point of the whittling down process is the need to establish a value yield. While many good ideas are necessarily dropped or delayed, budgets are open-ended. All companies have limited resources and this method is likely to yield the biggest return on investment.

6

SUPPLIER ENGAGEMENT OVERVIEW

EXECUTIVE SUMMARY: The greatest asset that the ICR process offers companies looking for a disciplined approach to cost reduction is its compression of time. This compression, however, has a price: Each step in the process is preceded by meticulous preparation.

Prior to the convening of the three supplier engagement modules a number of things need to be worked through so that the engagement process meets its time targets. Decisions need to be made on which suppliers should be engaged, how many suppliers should be engaged, what items should be studied, and where the actual engagement should take place. These are not things that should be allowed to wait until the engagement gets underway.

Prior to the breakout into three supplier modules, therefore, a logistics planning session needs to occur for the three specific supplier engagement modules. The object of this planning session is to finalize these details:

- Time, place, and participants.
- Duration of individual engagements.
- Meeting administrative logistics (invitations, travel plans, meeting room arrangements.
- Materials for engagements (who brings the specs, drawings, photos, etc.)

• • •

ICR IS NOT AN ALTERNATIVE APPROACH to cost reduction. Rather, it needs to be thought of as a structured tool for implementing cost reduction principles. Specifically, it aims at getting cost reduction principles into play quickly.

ICR does not take pot shots at VA/VE programs, early supplier involvement initiatives, or any of the pre-existing supplier cost reduction programs already in place. Most such programs have been well thought out and are vital to long-term corporate competitiveness. It is best to, think of the ICR process as one that condenses a great deal of knowledge about cost reduction into a very short concentrated event or "engagement."

ENGAGEMENT VS. INVOLVEMENT

Supplier engagement is the key instrument used in accomplishing that knowledge/time compression. In other words, success or failure in implementing ICR rides to a great extent on how expertly supplier engagement is implemented.

The term "engagement" is used to emphasize the reality that in ICR suppliers are more than involved in pleasant conversations about cost reduction or even detailed studies of potential cost savings. Rather, suppliers are being engaged face-to-face on ways to achieve very specific goals and objectives.

This supplier engagement process takes place across three different modules: VA/VE/design to cost, Six Sigma/lean manufacturing, and e-procurement/supply chain. Modules, depending on the personnel, subject matter, and complexity of material last one or two days and are held either at the customer's facilities or those of the supplier.

In planning for engagement, the engagement teams need to define the involvement of raw material suppliers, date and location of engagement, the personnel who will be attending, the agenda that will be followed (including prioritization of the parts to be discussed, pre-meeting tasks, and roles and responsibilities of those attending.

EARLY PLANNING

In cases where the parts to be studied number in the thousands or in cases where there are many potential suppliers available, a great deal of selectivity will need to be exercised. Engagement has to insure that appropriate areas of opportunity get appropriate attention, but the attention cannot be allowed to turn into a parody. It will be necessary to pick very selectively among the highest leveraged suppliers—the ones that are most connected to the product itself.

The ICR process is designed around production suppliers. This being so, in most cases it is not appropriate to consider MRO (maintenance, repair, and overhead) items in the engagements. (There are, however, some exceptions among a select number of non-manufacturing companies where MRO goods and services are a legitimate area of study.)

Another important early decision that must be made is how long to hold the engagement meetings—a day, two to three days, a week. Whatever the eventual determination, it has to be kept in mind that the power of these supplier engagements is that they are concentrated events held over as short a period of time as possible. Instead of weeks, months, and years, the objective at the beginning of a supplier engagement should be to compress the action into as short a time span as possible.

ENGAGEMENT'S VENUE

One major pre-meeting decision that requires considerable thought involves where the engagement itself will be held. Where it takes place—at the customer's facilities or at the supplier's facilities—is affected by a number of factors (see Figure 6-1).

FIGURE 6-1

ENGAGEMENT LOCATION CONSIDERATIONS

CUSTOMER FACILITY	SUPPLIER FACILITY
Design emphasis	Manufacturing process emphasis
Better access to customer people	Better access to supplier personnel
Availability of technical expertise	Availability of manufacturing expertise
Immediate feedback to design improvement ideas	Immediate feedback to mfg. process suggestions
Raw material supplier involvement	Raw material supplier involvement
Expose supplier to product assembly area	Expose customer personnel to supplier facility
No customer travel expenses	No supplier travel expenses

The focus that will be taken with each supplier will often dictate where the supplier engagement event will be held. If it's a mature product or the product is used by a highly regulated industry, it may not be possible to make many design changes. Nevertheless, it may still be possible to do a considerable amount of manufacturing process reengineering—e.g. moving equipment around, perhaps changing the tooling. If the decision is for a design focus, it will probably be a good idea for the suppliers to travel to the customers' facilities where all the design engineers are located. The biggest issue in many companies will be travel. Most companies won't be able to send all their engineers. More and more often, design is done by teams working on large systems. Even within large design departments there are specialists—such as materials and process people who key in on such areas as alloys, drafting, and dynamic loading. Large companies often have armies of engineering people. If that's going to be the focus, it won't be possible to bring an army of people to the supplier's facilities.

Conversely, if it's decided that the manufacturing process is more important than the design to cost focus and there's not going to be that much to design or redesign, then it may make more sense for the customer to bring a few people to the supplier's facilities and the most important thing for them to learn is how the product is manufactured. In that way key people will be able to walk the supplier's entire manufacturing process—with key people from the supplier explaining the tooling, the assembly, and how "these two parts don't fit together quite right." On the customer side, of course, many times it's helpful for suppliers who don't know where their product is being used to see the role it plays in the whole product. A lot of ideas can be brought to the surface simply by understanding how the supplier's product is used by the customer.

THE TIME FACTOR

A vital early decision that has to be made is how much time is to be spent on the project. In traditional VA/VE approaches, cost reduction is often a protracted process. It takes place in a "semi-random" design-redesign iterative loop over weeks, months, and years. In a typical design-oriented VA/VE undertaking, the customer usually begins the design of the product and calls in supplier "experts" as the need arises.

The ICR process starts (typically with an existing design) by bringing supplier engineers and customer engineers together before any design or redesign work commences. They need to be in a room with sample parts and spending one or two days going through every single part and drawing, identifying all the features that add value and all the features that don't add value in the engineering process.

When talking about the manufacturing process the supplier engagement leaders will want to map out all the process steps for a particular product. They will want to ask similar types of questions as in VA/VE discussions: Which manufacturing process steps add value and which don't add manufacturing value? They also will want to take the business procurement teams and have them meet face to face with the supplier representatives.

The amount of time to be spent on supplier engagement is dependent on how many parts and how complex the components are that will be dealt with here. Let's say a company wants to do the ICR process with twenty suppliers. Let's say that five or six of them build complex assemblies (5-axis robots, automobile dashboard assemblies, aircraft landing gear, etc.); 3 or 4 build simple components (PC boards, machined housings. connectors, etc.; 5 or 6 supply raw materials or semi-finished components (e.g. castings, forgings, stampings). Each of the complex assemblies may have 50 to 100 or more parts inside of it. It's going to be very difficult for anyone to evaluate all of those parts over a 1-2 day period. So it may be necessary to hold two 2-day sessions with suppliers in such cases, while ones with medium complex suppliers may end up with one, 2-day session, and one with simple raw materials suppliers may need to spend no more than one day—or even just a half a day. The point: Make the length of the sessions fit the products/suppliers under consideration.

WHAT ADDS VALUE?

Two or three supplier engagement sessions usually are going on in parallel. That's a major factor in keeping ICR on a fast track. With three sessions going on at the same time in parallel there are engineers talking to engineers about design to cost; customer and supplier manufacturing engineers; supply chain/ e-procurement staff interacting with business management leaders. Often three sessions are going on at the same time in parallel for four to eight hours. From these sessions the teams then develop a list of all the steps in their particular process that add value and all the steps that do not add value. The 3-Part value-added definition (see Chapter 2) must be employed to avoid fuzzy or subjective criteria and prevent arguments over which process steps may be eliminated.

After the list of value-added and non-value added steps is created the next thing that is done is the creation of an action plan listing what will be done to implement the suggestions. Suggestions usually take the form of eliminating the non-value adding steps in the design process, the manufacturing process, and supply chain and e-procurement process.

IMPLEMENTING ENGAGEMENT

Finally, it's time to implement the supplier engagement. This can be a smoothly functioning process or a nightmare. It depends on the thoroughness of the preparation.

When many people conduct a VA/VE type event, they contact the supplier and say, "I'm coming over to your plant and I'd like to do a VA/VE analysis of this part. I'll be there next week, please have your engineers ready." The trouble with such an approach is that if you haven't spent much time getting ready for the event, upon arrival, you must initiate discussions of why are we here and what are the ground rules. The meeting is chaotic as people scramble about gathering documents, routings, getting the "experts" into the conference room, etc.—all the things that should have taken place ahead of time.

The point is that in preparing for engagement it's important to retrace the ground covered at the senior management engagement and during the preparation. The leader of the supplier engagement should have already talked about the constraints, about the things the customer will allow, about how much risk the company is willing to tolerate. If all of these things have been covered up front, then the engagement leader will have actually sent copies to the supplier of the decisions made during the management engagement. He/she also will have sent a checklist of things to do ahead of time—e.g. pull drawings, tooling, quality history, process routing sheets. The engagement leader also will have prepared a checklist of his/her own preparitory things to do—e.g. taking photos of supplier's product being installed, printing his/her own specifications, etc.

Finally, it will be necessary to put together an effective meeting plan that includes such basics as making sure that conference room(s) is/are available, flip charts are in every room,

Fig. 6-2: ICR Supplier Engagement, Pre-Event Checklist

The following list represents a pre-ICR event checklist. It is designed to clearly state the action items and data required before a successful ICR event may be conducted.

Item	Activity	Assigned To	Complete
	Customer Pre-Event Preparations		
1	Determine part numbers to be reviewed	Customer Team	
2	Prepare Supplier Spend report - "Top10 Part Spend"	Customer Team	
3	Prepare spread sheet - "ICR - Supplier Information"	Customer Team	
4	Route to <<Company Name>> members for the input from their disciplines	Customer Team	
5	"ICR - Supplier Information" Complete	Customer Team	
6	Obtain digital images of supplier's parts, installed in end-items	Customer Team	
7	Gather quality data on subject parts	Customer Team	
8	Current price and contract out year pricing	Customer Team	
9	Determine target costs	Customer Team	
10	Prepare presentation to supplier's media availability	Customer Team	
11	Print Supplier Scorecard data	Customer Team	
12	Presentation additions for specific supplier	Customer Team	
	Customer to Supplier Communication		
13	Introduction letter and addendum personalized and sent	Customer Team	
14	Date confirmation communication with supplier	Customer Team	
15	Logistics surrounding suppliers facility - who, where, when	Supplier Team	
16	Determine dress code at suppliers' facility	Supplier Team	
17	Determine media format - electronic, overheads, etc.	Supplier Team	
	Supplier Pre-Event Preparations		
18	Obtain drwgs. and specs. Of subject parts	Supplier Team	
19	Sub-tier supplier information (what, who, how, cost)	Supplier Team	
20	Cost break-down (labor, materials, overhead) Note: No need to include SG&A or profit. Actual dollars are not necessary. A pie chart reflecting the manufacturing cost breakdown by percentage is most helpful. This information will be used to help focus the discussions on the highest cost drivers of the components or assemblies.	Supplier Team	
21	Manufacturing Process routing (maps) for each of the part numbers	Supplier Team	
	Trip Planning		
22	Date selection	Customer and Supplier	
23	<<Company Name>> team availability	Customer Team	
24	Date selection firmed	Customer Team	
25	Travel plans and reservations made (plane, hotel, car, etc...)	Customer Team	

marker boards are in every room. These are just the obvious logistics of putting on a successful engagement—logistics that many people forget and then find themselves spending the first hours of the supplier engagement trying to find projectors, flip charts, drawings, sample parts, etc.

When the engagement starts there should be no confusion about exactly what's required. Sample parts will need to be available on the table, along with drawings, the routing, and the tooling. The people on the shop floor will already have been notified that at "10 o'clock "we're going to be bringing the customers through for a three hour process map study. We will be going through every single operation so in some cases union representatives will need to be notified."

Such things sound trivial, but they're the trivial things that make or break successful engagements. They need to be finalized before meeting with suppliers. In fact, a detailed agenda of all the things you will be doing in the morning and afternoon should be published and agreed to by the supplier. Once there is agreement by the supplier a detailed agenda can be prepared.

WHO WILL ATTEND?

The final decision that will need to be made is who will be involved in supplier engagement. Early up-front at the senior manager engagement, a list of ICR team members should have been put together. Depending on what the focus will be—e.g. manufacturing, design-to- cost—the project leader will need to decide precisely which people are needed to physically participate in the engagement.

If, for example, the focus will be on design-to-cost, the primary engineer with design responsibilities will need to attend

Fig. 6-3: Typical 2-Day Supplier Engagement

	Day 1	Day 2
AM	• ICR Overview and Event Familiarization – 2 hr • "As-Is" Process Mapping – On the floor with chosen part (include up-front order interpretation / material planning / production control activities) – 2 hr	• Design & Mfg Team resent the results of the ICR Forms, Process Mapping using assign VA / NVA – 2 hr • Formulate procurement and mfg improvement ideas – 2 hr • Design Team discuss "As-Is" design – 2 hr (run in parallel with Mfg session)
PM	• "As-Is" Process Mapping (cont) – Other sub-assys. or details of end item – 4 hr • Entry of process mapping data onto "ICR Forms – Process Mapping" – (2 hrs) • Begin formation of improvement ideas – (1 hr)	• "To-Be" Design Process and Barriers / complete formation of design-to-cost ideas – 1.5 hr (run in parallel with Mfg session) • Mfg and Design Teams "merge" on design "To-Be" – 1.5 hr • Integrate all ideas into improvement opportunities and create Action Plan – 1 hr • De-brief results of event and create minutes and action plans – 1.5 hr

all three days. Similarly with manufacturing engagement the person with primary manufacturing responsibility will need to attend all three days. In addition, it's important to spell out who all the key people involved are and their support staffs. Most of these people will continue with their regular jobs, but will be ready to participate when their contribution is required. A good idea is to spell out in the agenda who will be needed for portions of the engagement.

A TYPICAL SUPPLIER ENGAGEMENT

The four case studies at the back of the book describe in detail various engagements. In this section we will only briefly describe a "typical" supplier engagement. If the product or assembly is relatively complex, the team probably does a Pareto analysis or cost breakdown. The Pareto, which looks like a bill of materials, is used to separate out the most expensive parts of an assembly from the least costly parts of the product or assembly. If, for instance, a Pareto is used to analyze a fully "stuffed" auto dashboard panel assembly selling for $1500, the Pareto might show that the most expensive components in the dashboard assembly are the gages—at a cost of around $250—followed by the air conditioning, stereo components, and other control components. Among the least expensive components in the dashboard assembly might be the brackets and the wiring harness clamps.

A Pareto analysis would put the costs of all the major parts of the assembly on a bar graph—from most expensive to least expensive—to graphically indicate where to start. The Pareto points to the areas where the greatest cost reduction payoff probably lies. (Pareto graphing can be used on suppliers as well as components.)

Based on Pareto analysis, the team focuses on developing a specific list of components and specific suppliers and a detailed supplier engagement action plan and team members begin working on the opportunities highlighted in the Pareto analysis. Looking over the Pareto, the team determines that the greatest opportunities will lie in gages and switches (design rather than manufacturing because not a lot of manufacturing is involved in producing either). To investigate gages and switches will involve two groups of suppliers.

Now the question becomes how much time do you have to make this project work? Senior management gives the team three months. Not a lot of time! So the team decides to have one group of people meeting with the gage suppliers and another group of engineers meeting with switch suppliers on the same day at your facility. Everyone is brought in for a two-day event.

Essentially the presenters go through the same charts—introduction and engagement—that they went through at the senior manager level. It does the exact same thing for suppliers—setting the stage and expectations for engagement.

Then the meeting breaks up into two groups. In this instance they are a gage supplier group and a switch supplier group. The team may decide that since the same engineers in their facility design the gages as design the switches it isn't feasible to break up into two groups, so its necessary to do one after the other. On day one the gage suppliers meet with the team and on day two the switch makers have their day. This is all part of getting ready for the supplier engagement.

One thing that needs to be pointed out here is that while the ICR process makes great sense for the Fortune 100 companies, it is just as appropriate for use at a more modest level by smaller companies (those with sales in the $50 million to $250 million range. What the ICR process does so well is it breaks down gi-ant cost problems into smaller pieces.

While some may think in terms of 25+ people in a conference room, ICR really functions best in smaller engagements—often with fewer than ten people. In most cases small companies could thrive on the disciplined approach that ICR provides.

7

SUPPLIER ENGAGEMENT IN DESIGN

EXECUTIVE SUMMARY: The design-to-cost module is aimed at identifying systemic and unique design improvement opportunities that can reduce or eliminate part or part family cost drivers. It gets to this point by prioritizing cost reduction opportunities and creating a detailed action plan that achieves cost savings through design optimization.

To get to this point, the design-to-cost module starts from the premise that customer value can be optimized by minor (or major) design modifications and seeking answers to these kinds of questions:

- What other materials could be used?
- Can we use an industry or company standard part?
- Can we minimize non-standard specifications?
- Can this assembly be simplified?
- Can we combine parts?
- Can we eliminate non-value added features?

- Can we reduce or eliminate inspection?
- Can we modify to reduce scrap?
- Is new technology available that might reduce cost?
- Should the features/functions of this component be combined into a higher assembly?

The purpose of all this questioning is to arrive at a small, but powerful, list of design-to-cost changes, which are then prioritized by use of a 2x2 matrix (see Figure 7-2).

• • •

SUPPLIER ENGAGEMENT IN DESIGN differs little (mostly not at all) from a traditional VA/VE process. Therefore, if the company has an on-site VA/VE or design to cost group, it should be encouraged to take the leadership position in this portion of the ICR process. Likewise, suppliers should be encouraged to send representatives with VA/VE or design-to-cost experience to the supplier engagement in design process.

Showing deference to the good work that each company has done in developing its own in-house VA/VE process can pay off richly, not just in cooperation, but in the actual cost reduction ideas developed during the analytical stages of the process. This is more than an exercise in avoiding stepping on people's toes. Ideally such experienced people should take lead positions in the ICR supplier engagement in design module.

A supplier engagement in design, works from an agenda that follows a script similar to the one outlined in Chapter 6 (see Figure 6-3). The design to cost team will spend four hours or so together. Engineers from the suppliers and from the customers will gather together in a room. In that room are sample parts, specifications, and technical experts in such areas as materials, manufacturing processes, stress, dynamics, and software.

The session opens with an explanation by the module leader of what is going to be done in the next four hours or so and how the group will go about doing it. First comes the objective which is to identify system-wide and unique design improvement opportunities that can reduce or eliminate part or part family cost drivers. This is followed by a description of deliverables, which are prioritized cost reduction opportunities and detailed action plans to achieve the targeted savings through design optimization.

Then the leader of the engagement in design launches into the five steps that will be used to identify the cost drivers and reduce or eliminate them. The process steps are:

1. Analyze the current design.
2. Define cost reduction alternatives.
3. Identify barriers to cost reduction solutions.
4. Prioritize cost reduction opportunities.
5. Refine and integrate proposed solutions.

DESIGN TO-COST MODULE, STEP 1: DESIGN ANALYSIS

The objective of the analysis step is to define the design constraints, requirements, and "as designed" costs. Key deliverables will fall in the area of design constraints and requiremnets, "as designed" cost drivers, "as designed" performance evaluation, design-related quality issues, and potential areas for improvement. Among the tools and techniques available for this step: "as designed" team review, drawing/specification review, design to cost checklist, manufacturing process review (see www.icrprocess.com for templates and checklists).

If the team has done its preparation correctly, it already knows what its cost breakdown for this particular assembly is and what the drivers are. In this case, then, it concentrates its attention on the "as designed" cost drivers. Suppose, for example, that in a particular assembly 35% of the cost of this assembly is in the machined housing. That's its number one cost driver! (The team will want to spend a good deal of its time looking at that housing.)

A design-to-cost checklist can be used in the analysis. In looking at the "as is" design the team will want to see if there are any non-value adding requirements that can be eliminated or if there are any inspections that can be modified, reduced, or eliminated. Are there any fixed processes that need to be modified, improved, or eliminated? Are non-industry standard specifications being used (e.g. the company's own grade of metal rather than an ASTM or SAE standard that's readily available). In most cases if the designer knew how much the special grade increased the cost he/she would be willing to take a standard off-the-shelf substitute. Is it possible to reduce or eliminate costly nondestructive or destructive testing (x-ray, ultrasound, etc.)? Is there something that can be done to eliminate or reduce scrap and rework?

The team will also want to ask questions about the use of standard parts in lieu of custom parts. Can an existing "off-the-shelf" part be substituted? Can more effective material be substituted? Even using a standard material or part is not always the best, if a more cost-effective substitute is available. For instance, is there a material or part being used elsewhere in the company that could be substituted, thus taking advantage of a volume price break?

During this analysis portion of the engagement it may be useful to focus on opportunities to increase the value by adding functionality to the product. This is where it might be advisable to have a marketing person on call to help in explaining what customers truly value in a particular component or product.

DESIGN-TO-COST MODULE, STEP 2: COST REDUCTION ALTERNATIVES

Defining cost reduction alternatives involves identifying design-related alternatives, risks, and benefits. Key deliverables are design alternatives, risks, and benefits; optimization of design and manufacturing processes to achieve best value; completion of a design-to-cost checklist; and a design-to-cost idea summary for alternatives that require significant effort and/or senior management approval. Among the tools and techniques that can be used are brainstorming, design for manufacture and assembly (DFMA), Pareto analysis, design to cost summary worksheets, design to cost checklists.

Typically a team might be looking to modify, reduce, or eliminate special processes or special materials and the supplier indicates that "we only buy 1000 lb. per year of this material but 100,000 lb. per year of this." The question that needs to be asked here is "what would be the impact of using this other material? Is that going to degrade our product in terms of strength of the material, performance, reliability, or cost of warranty? If not, could the design be modified to allow the lower cost material without compromising customer satisfaction?

Please note: Although we typically use "mechanical" component terminology in our examples, "electrical" design and component issues are addressed exactly the same in the ICR process. One notable exception is the issue of electrical component obsolescence, which can drive very expensive "lifetime buys" of active or passive components. The PCB/PWB designs may need to be changed to prevent this situation. In addition, the designer should do everything possible to avoid custom connectors or specialty colored or gage wire, etc.

By exchanging one material for another there should be a trade-off discussion. What's the benefit of using this material vs. the one we're using today? Is there a risk vs. benefit analysis already prepared or underway? If not, the team may want to make its own list of benefits vs. risks. A typical cost/benefit review might involve comparing a part made with a customized grade of aluminum with one made with a standard grade. The analysis would summarize and quantify the benefits in these areas: unit cost savings, performance, quality, and cycle time. An important point should be made about cost-benefit analysis: It will be impossible in a short 2-day ICR event to be 100% accurate in quantifying cost savings. Therefore, a "rough order of magnitude" estimate will need to be used to prioritize the opportunities for further study and more detailed financial analysis.

DESIGN-TO-COST MODULE, STEP 3: BARRIERS AND SOLUTIONS

The objective of step three is to identify barriers to implementation of cost reductions and defining of solutions or counter-measures that would enable successful implementation of the design modification. The deliverables are: the barriers to implementation of optimum design, root cause analysis, and solutions to eliminate barriers with "ROM" scope, budget, and schedule impact.

A typical barrier might involve changing a group of materials from a customized material to a standard off-the-shelf material. So what are the barriers? Does the team have to conduct an analysis of the design to insure that there's no impact on performance, weight, operability, warranties, or safety? Will the customers have any adverse reaction to changing this material or this component? Is there going to be an issue of availability? If the company is using an off-the-shelf component or assembly instead of a custom design, is it, in fact, available off the shelf? Will it be necessary to redesign, recertify, requalify? Is customer approval required for any "form, fit, or function changes?

All these questions need to be posed to determine how big the barriers are. Ultimately, (though this is done briefly during ICR, it is fully done later) root cause analysis (looking at each of these particular barriers and finding out what has to be done to solve the problem) will have to be employed. Barriers will need to be probed to determine whether they are real or simply excuses for not changing something. In regulated industries (energy, medical, and aerospace, especially), engineering people often are tempted to throw such governing regulatory worries out on the table to slow up progress on something not to their liking. These barriers—real or fancied—have to be examined to determine whether they're smokescreens or real issues. Issues often look bigger than they really are. Indeed, in many cases the barriers turn out to involve little more than some additional paperwork.

The reason ICR is such a successful tool is that its practitioners try to answer as many of these questions as they can right in the engagement meeting—long before they become real limitations. Another reason is practitioners usually are satisfied with an approximate answer today rather than waiting for a perfect answer that will take six months. It's okay to use approximate numbers at the cost engagement. Good approximate numbers allow the engagement team to say something like this: "Based on Pareto analysis of the design team, these are the top five ideas that we want to pursue." You don't need perfect numbers at this stage of the design to cost engagement. Approximate numbers will do.

DESIGN-TO-COST MODULE, STEP 4: WHAT COMES FIRST?

At this step in the design-to-cost process, practitioners should have a completed checklist and a one-page idea summary for each of the design ideas completed. The objective of the "prioritize cost reduction opportunities" step is to have assessed, quantified, and prioritized all opportunities requiring significant effort and/or senior management approval. Deliverables include a feasibility ranking matrix (Figure 7-1) completed for significant effort opportunities—opportunities ranked and prioritized, and action items and responsibilities assigned. Tools and techniques include 2x2 risk/benefit matrix (Figure 7-2 brainstorming, Pareto analysis, feasibility ranking matrix, and ICR meeting minutes form.

The 2x2 matrix (Figure 7-2) is a very simple, yet powerful, tool to achieve the most important key to successful implementation of any ICR project—focused attention and prioritization on the ideas with the biggest return on investment. The 2x2 matrix probably requires some explanation. Here's how it works: On the Y-axis, we measure Risk and/or Cost to implement each proposed idea. On the X-axis, we make a first-order approximation for the cost-savings potential of each idea.

The matrix forces the ICR team to make some tough decisions before it even completes its initial engagement about which ideas should receive the most attention, which should come second, and even those ideas that will not get worked at all. It is important that the 2x2 prioritization matrix is com-

Fig. 7-1: Feasibility Ranking Matrix (aka "Prioritization Factors")

Idea	Time to Implement Idea (5 = 1+yr; 3 = 6-12Mo; 1 = <6mo)	Engineering Analysis Cost (5 = $100K+; 3 = $50-100; 1 = <$25K)	Number of Parts Req'd to ReDesign (5 = 10+; 3 = 5-10; 1 = <3)	Total Cost/Risk to Implement (15 = Max)	"Relative" Total Cost to Implement (1-100)
1. Material Substitution SS302 to SS304	2	2	1	5	33 (5/15 x 100)
2. Change from Machined Aluminum to Cast Alum	4	5	2	11	73 (11/15 x 100)
3. Replace custom fastener with commercially available version	1	1	1	3	20 (3/15 x 100)

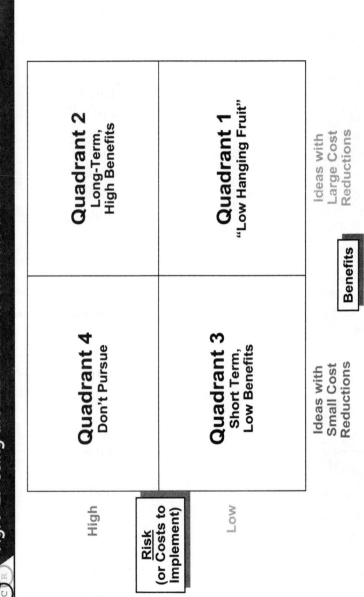

Fig. 7-2: Using the 2x2 Matirx to estimate the risks vs. benefits

pleted AFTER the ideas are generated. Otherwise the creative brainstorming process will not generate enough good ideas and a "game-changer" idea may never get mentioned for fear that it will seem too risky. Only when all the ideas are compared to each other, will the ICR team know which ideas are better or worse. The following example illustrates the concept.

The values of the Y-axis are created based on prioritization weighting factors that were established during the senior management engagement (Chapter 4). By taking the sum of all the columns for a particular idea the team gets a "total risk/cost to implement." Further, by dividing the total by the max possible score and then multiplying by 100, puts all of the ideas on "Relative" scale of 1-100. The following example illustrates this concept:

By setting the Y-axis range from 1 to 100 in the above example, we have been able to plot the relative "cost/risk" of each of the proposed ideas. This does NOT mean that the "low-relative-risk" ideas (in this example #1 and #3) would automatically be implemented. Rather, this would focus the teams' efforts on the most likely candidates first and after a thorough evaluation would decide to proceed or abandon each idea. Plotting these results on the 2x2 matrix gives us the specific example shown in Figure 3.

Similarly the X-axis is established based on the relative cost reduction potential of each idea. Rough order of magnitude (ROM) cost savings estimates are all that are required. Once again, not all of the "home-run" cost reduction ideas would automatically be implemented, but would be balanced against relative risk and then studied further. Once all the ideas are plotted on a 2x2 matrix, it's time for the team to get down to the important work of prioritizing the ideas and creating initial action plans for implementing the ideas with the best potential return on investment and the most manageable risk profile.

Fig. 7-3: 2x2 Cost vs. benefits for Sample ICR Ideas

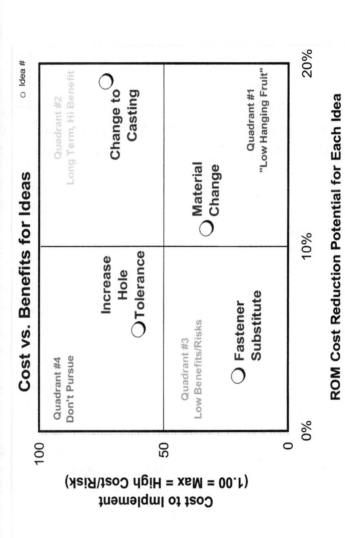

Cost vs. Benefits for Ideas

Applying the matrix to the grades of aluminum in an aeronautics part we can get a pretty good idea about how changes in use of a particular alloy from one grade of aluminum to another affect part cost. Is it a very low cost saving idea or not a low cost saving idea? One grade costs \$4/lb and the other \$3.50/lb. If it's a \$4/lb. grade and a change is made to a grade costing \$2/lb, that's a 50% saving.

Using the 2x2 matrix in risk/benefit analysis allows users to sort out ideas by their relative risk/cost relationships. Each idea can be sorted into one of these four quadrants:

Quadrant 1 is the place to be. The cost savings is maximized, risk is minimized. This is the area pursued first. The low-hanging fruit.

Quadrant 2. Upper right hand quadrant produces tremendous cost savings, but it's high risk. (Long term, though there may be a way around that risk.

Quadrant 3. This may be some stuff that's easy to do, but there's not going to be a huge savings. However, since it's so easy to do, it may be worth the little effort that's involved.

Quadrant 4. This is stuff you'll never do. It's high risk and low benefit.

TURNING IDEAS INTO ACTIONS

Without disparaging consultants, one typical complaint against consultants is that "they show up and tell you what to do, write big thick reports and then leave their clients with all the work." This is not the process of ICR. The purpose of the ICR process is two-fold: uncover heretofore unseen cost reduction ideas and then implement them and achieve cost reductions. One of the biggest reasons why so many continuous improvement initiatives have failed is that their proponents fail to recognize how challenging it is to prioritize and take actions in the face of day-to-day business actions. Teams go off-site and brainstorm a dozen "world-hunger" projects to dramatically improve their business and while they are gone, all of the e-mail, voice-mail, and in-boxes continue to fill up. What's needed is a systematic method to sort through the dozens of ideas and prioritize the ones that have immediate benefits, list the longer term projects that will need to be followed up on and, most important, to "kill" those ideas that will likely be a waste of time and resources.

One proposed cure is the creation of a RAIL (rolling action item list) that lists the specific actions, accountable persons and due dates. A typical RAIL has only four to five columns on a spreadsheet and is reviewed weekly by the ICR team leader and kept up-to-date as actions are closed or new actions appear.

The last thing that takes place at the design to cost engagement is actual ranking and prioritizing of opportunities. Action items and responsibilities are assigned. In the design to cost idea summary (see *www.icrprocess.com* for idea summary worksheet) we talked about the barriers and limitations for each of these ideas. And we talked about the solutions to the barriers.

But one thing that needs to be made very clear is there is no room here for generic solutions. Solutions must be very specific. The ICR process is not designed for the entire company. It's designed for a particular product. So on this particular product we've looked at the design-to-cost module and identified this particular grade of material that's $4/lb. and another that's $3.50/lb. The solution to the barrier is straightforward: We have to change the drawing and the parts list and include this new material. So the solution is that Joe, who is in the room, needs to go change the drawing. Sal who also is in the room has to change the parts list. Anne who works for Sal has to process all the paperwork and get supervisory approval needed to make the change. (All done within a prescribed time.) Many TQM teams talk about things that need to be done, but never put together an action plan to put them together.

DESIGN- TO-COST,
STEP 5: MAKING SOLUTIONS FIT

The final step, refining and integrating proposed solutions, involves refining proposed solutions and integrating them with ideas from the manufacturing process module. The two key deliver ables are documentation of proposed solutions and integration of the solutions with manufacturing process opportunities.

Success of ICR requires to a very great extent a very high level of synergy between design engineering teams and manufacturing teams. In some ICR engagements, both of those teams are merged together into a single team. In other engagements the teams work separately, but then get back together to implement all of their ideas.

This way the teams often are able to catch and correct any overlap and redundancy before each team "steps on each other's toes." Design and manufacturing processes are so inextricably linked in most companies that it's very difficult to separate the two. Whether tight linking is good or bad is probably a decision that needs to be made at the ICR program management level.

Tools and techniques used at this step include: brainstorming, milestone plans (road maps), Gantt charts (graphical representations with all the actions and due dates depicted), and Parato analysis. The final deliverable for all the teams is a 2x2 risk vs. benefit matrix, a list of ideas, costs to implement, savings, and action plan.

SUPPLIER ENGAGEMENT
IN MANUFACTURING AND SIX SIGMA

EXECUTIVE SUMMARY: The manufacturing engagement seeks to define the most optimal manufacturing process for each part or part family and define the changes that are needed to put them into effect. Once done, the engagement team puts together a detailed action plan, by part family or component, to achieve savings through optimization of the manufacturing process. Engagement teams also use Six Sigma techniques to search out opportunities to reduce the cost of poor quality (COPQ) by reducing or eliminating such things as scrap, re-work, repair, or redundant inspections. Teams follow lean manufacturing principles based on the "Toyota Production System" to search out and reduce wastes in seven areas: motion, processing, overproduction, waiting, re-work, transportation and inventory.

In making the diagnosis and setting and prescribing the remedy, the team leans heavily on such questioning as:

- Can some process steps be simplified, combined, or eliminated?
- What process steps are non-value added?
- Could outsourcing of "non-core" components/assemblies reduce cost, floorspace, or overhead?
- Are standard labor learning curves applied?
- Can the cost of special processes (anodizing, heat treatment, plating, etc.) be reduced by using industry standard processing?
- How well is the manufacturing staff deploying lean manufacturing and/or Six Sigma quality improvement processes?
- Are inspection or testing processes excessive?
- Can the raw material be modified or standardized to reduce total cost?

Optimally the questioning will lead to: elimination of redundant and non-value processes, consideration of new technology manufacturing alternatives, elimination of excessive handling, and consideration of outsourcing opportunities.

• • •

THERE ARE TWO BIG DIFFERENCES between the engagement described in chapter seven and the manufacturing Six Sigma module. In the design-to-cost module, the meeting is held in a conference room with drawings on the table. The best place to conduct this module is at the supplier's facility and preferably on the supplier's factory floor. After the introduction of team members, and during this engagement, team members will want to have a process map pre-prepared for the particular component or assembly, or it may be necessary to create a process map on the spot (see Chapter 2).

The second difference is the strategy and emphasis. Where the objective for design-to-cost was to identify design improvement opportunities to reduce or eliminate cost drivers, here it's to define an optimum manufacturing process for each part or part family. In many (probably most) cases it may not be necessary to alter the design in any way. The only major change may be restricted to re-arranging, shortening, and reducing work in the manufacturing process.

The essence of the manufacturing/Six Sigma engagement is to increase manufacturing throughput in two ways: (1) by using "lean" techniques to reduce cycle time and non-value added labor; and (2) by using advanced "Six Sigma" problem solving tools to reduce wasted labor (a.k.a. scrap, re-work, repair) caused by quality problems. The "hidden factory" is an expression traditionally used to describe all of the additional unwritten process steps (polishing, reinstalling, adjusting, replacing, reworking, finding, etc.) in every company that is required to actually produce acceptable parts to the customer's requirements. The hidden factory has been rechristened the "cost of poor quality (COPQ) and has been estimated to be somewhere between 25% and 35% of total revenue in typical North American companies that are operating at 3.0 Sigma Quality level (93% overall acceptance level or first-pass-yield). As such, the manufacturing/Six-Sigma engagement has an opportunity to dramatically improve the bottom line of any manufactured product.

To attack the 25–35% COPQ opportunity, the manufacturing/ Six Sigma engagement follows almost all of the steps of the design-to-cost engagement (see Chapter 7), but the emphasis is different. Instead of looking at changes in product design, we are looking at changes in the manufacturing process. The tangible work-product of this engagement is a list of potential manufacturing process changes such as tooling and/or fixtures, method sheets, inspection procedures, special process settings, physical factory lay-out, set-up reduction /improvements, etc. These process changes will require discrete action items and a timeline for implementation, similar to the design-to-cost module. In fact, some ICR supplier engagements have successfully combined the manufacturing and design-to-cost engagement together into one module conducted by the same team.

Many companies today have lean manufacturing programs already in place and many have in-house experts or may use outside consultants. And, as we indicated in the design-to-cost module, if your company has in-house experts in lean manufacturing they should be the ones to lead this process. The ICR process in this module is virtually identical with the lean manufacturing process based on the Toyota production system in use at many companies.

As we noted above, at the heart of lean manufacturing is the need to eliminate waste in the manufacturing process. Eliminating non-value adding steps is the key to successful implementation of lean manufacturing. As we explained in Chapter 2, the only operations that are defined as "value-added" in lean manufacturing are steps that (1) change the component or assembly in some way, (2) are done right the first time, and (3) the customer is willing to pay for. As with the design-to-cost module, the leader of the manufacturing module follows a five-step approach to identifying and eliminating the manufacturing cost drivers. The five process steps that are followed in the lean manufacturing module are:

1. a. Analysis of the current manufacturing processes.
   b. Analysis of current quality issues.

2. Defining of manufacturing alternatives to improve cycle time, throughout, or yield.
3. Identification of barriers and proposal of solutions.
4. Prioritization of cost reduction opportunities.
5. Refinement and integration of solutions.

STEP 1A: THE CURRENT "AS-IS" MANUFACTURING PROCESS

The objective of the "as-is" analysis step is to review or create the process map of the current manufacturing process. The key deliverables include the defining of manufacturing constraints and requirements, defining of the "as designed" manufacturing process, identification of historical manufacturing process issues and problems, identification of potential areas for improvement, and a spelling out of the major manufacturing cost drivers. By having the supplier and customer in the same room talking about the same issues, each learns things never realized before.

During this step in the lean manufacturing module, these sorts of questions need to be asked about the manufacturing process:

- Is a process flow chart available?
- Is the manufacturing process clearly defined?
- Can some process steps be simplified, combined, eliminated?
- Are some process steps non-value added?
- Can secondary operations be modified or eliminated?
- Are standard labor learning curves applied?

While the above list appears to be little more than self evi-
dent self examination, having participated in more than fifty
lean supplier engagements, we still find it remarkable how little
thought has actually gone into many of the items under question. Take for instance item two in the above list. A fair number
of companies are making parts where specs have never actually
been spelled out. Many times orders come in for a part saying,
"make per blueprint," and they're given to a machinist who
makes the part. This is very common in low volume production operations. That's why its an important factor in the ICR
process to get the actual production supervisors together at
least once to discuss how the parts are being made.

The three value-adding criteria discussed above is another
area that often elicits more talk than action. In truth there are
many manufacturing steps that are done but don't really add
value. They're done because similar steps have been done on
a similar item. For instance, some companies prime a part and
then paint it. Are both steps needed? Could there be a better
grade of paint that would allow them to skip the priming? If
the base aluminum is anodized first, is priming and painting
needed at all? Some companies have as many as four painting
steps. Customized business jets can be painted and repainted
a dozen times. Is it possible to get rid of at least some of these
steps? These are the kinds of specific questions that need to be
asked during the analysis.

STEP 1B: ANALYSIS OF THE CURRENT QUALITY ISSUES

As noted earlier, the goal of lean principles is to reduce the sev-
en forms of waste. Typical implementations of lean manufacturing, with their emphasis on cycle time and inventory reduction

fail to address three key wastes that Six Sigma techniques have made their focus: rework, unnecessary processing, and over-production. Nearly every MRP system instructs the factory/suppliers to overbuild (via safety stock) to allow for less than perfect yield due to quality failures. In many industries, this overproduction can amount to 40-50% of the required demand. Imagine if you threw away $500 for every $1000 you made in salary, how long would you allow this trend to continue? Yet, company after company in many different industries make it a policy to "overbuild" to allow for poor yield.

For these reasons, the ICR process recognizes that taking an integrated approach to cost reduction, requires attacking all seven forms of waste ("MUDA" as defined in Chapter 2) in the manufacturing/Six-Sigma engagements. Principles of Six Sigma: such as failure modes and effects analysis (FMEA), paired-comparisons, measurement system evaluation (MSE) and even the simple application of DMAIC (define, measure, analyze, improve, and control) can all help to lower the cost if poor quality (COPQ). After, or during, the ICR team's analysis of the current manufacturing process, a number of questions need to be asked about quality of the product in question:

- Is the cost-of-poor-quality (COPQ) being measured and broken down into its three elements of: internal failures, external failures and appraisal costs?
- Are inspection (appraisal) requirements improving quality or just adding additional costs?
- Are there built-in rework processes (i.e. "hidden factory") that are masking quality non-conformance?
- Can these non-conformances be reduced or eliminated by more robust fixturing, in-process testing, operator train-ing, etc.?

- Are industry-standard quality requirements being used, or are we requiring customized "one-off" requirements that add unnecessary costs?
- Are quality improvement teams, quality circles, quality action teams, etc., working on the biggest drivers of COPQ or just fire fighting?

Once the above questions are answered during the ICR engagement, numerous opportunities will be found for lowering COPQ and achieving some of the substantial financial benefits reported by many pioneering implementers of Six Sigma processes (GE, Honeywell, Motorola, etc.).

While the ICR process is not set up to replace Six Sigma or other quality programs, ICR DOES offer a practical framework for integrating Six Sigma methodology into other cost reduction initiatives (lean manufacturing, VA/VE, supply chain, etc).

STEP 2: DEFINING THE ALTERNATIVES

The objective of process step 2 (defining manufacturing and quality alternatives) is to creatively challenge each team member to identify manufacturing alternatives that reduce cost, cycle time, or improve COPQ. Among the deliverables on the table:

- Elimination of redundant and non-value added processess.
- Evaluation of new technology or processing alternatives.
- Elimination of excessive handling and inspection.
- A complete manufacturing process checklist.
- A manufacturing process idea summary for alternatives that require significant effort and/or program approval.

STEP 3: BARRIERS AND SOLUTIONS

Step three in lean manufacturing is identical to step 3 in design to cost: identify barriers and propose solutions.

Four things need to be nosed out in this step: (1) Barriers to implementation need to be identified, (2) Root cause analysis needs to be performed, (3) Solutions to eliminate barriers need to be identified, and (4) Consensus reached on optimum manufacturing processes.

STEP 4: PRIORITIZATION

The objective of step 4 is to define and prioritize proposed manufacturing cost reduction opportunities. These opportunities occur in two forms: those requiring significant effort and management/customer approval (assessed, quantified, and prioritized) and action items to capture all other ideas assigned.

Key deliverables to be strived for include a feasibility ranking matrix completed for significant effort opportunities, opportunities ranked and prioritized, and action items and responsibilities assigned.

STEP 5: REFINING AND INTEGRATING

In process step 5 the team works on refining solutions and integrating them with solutions identified in the design to cost module. Deliverables include: solutions integrated with design to cost opportunities and documentation of proposed solutions. As we indicated earlier in the book, it is possible to conduct the design-to-cost and manufacturing/Six Sigma engagements simultaneously.

9

ENGAGEMENT SUPPLY CHAIN
AND E-PROCUREMENT

EXECUTIVE SUMMARY: Here is where ICR is radically different from traditional VA/VE or lean approaches to supply cost reduction. The ICR process actually proposes assisting suppliers to improve their own sub-tier supplier management. Many suppliers don't have size or sophistication to successfully implement many of the supply-chain management tools that their customers have used for years.

Where the previously described modules looked at reducing costs via the way products are designed or manufactured, this module looks at cost reduction from a business and systems point of view. It aims at reducing transaction costs at every step of the purchasing process and uses new electronic tools to eliminate and reduce them. In addition it uses the market savvy of the purchasing/supply/sourcing function(s) to bring about cost savings based on more intelligent leveraging of supplier power. Ideally this module is aimed at reducing costs for the supplier as well as the customer.

To understand the power of supply chain management and e-procurement tools to bring about mega cost reductions, one only needs to look at how the supply chain and its use of the many new e-procurement tools are changing the landscape.

Unlike the two modules previously discussed, the supply chain/e-procurement supplier engagement has fewer technicians and more business and supply chain participants. Instead of discussing how products are designed and/or made, the thinking here centers around what takes place in procuring the appropriate goods and services. Specifically this module deals with the supply strategies and business issues involved in sourcing, buying, and managing goods and services moving in and out of the company. The engagement team will be looking for ways that give companies employing ICR a competitive advantage. Much of what will be discussed in this module will center on examining how business practices contribute or detract from customer and supplier competitiveness.

One thing that needs to be noted early on in discussing the supply chain/e-procurement engagement module is that it is not about traditional price leveraging where customers demand price concessions and suppliers who need the business acquiesce. When suppliers are forced to reduce prices by eating margins, costs are not really reduced, merely moved, and will bounce back again.

Corporate supply chain initiatives have been launched in almost every *Fortune 500* company since the 1990s. Most have focused on four primary methods of price reduction, but few case studies portray the reality of what happens when a company chooses to implement one of these four approaches without lowering the true cost of the product:

1. Re-negotiation, which by itself, is typically just "margin transfer" has these unintended consequences:
   - Suppliers recover their losses during the next economic upturn or by overcharging for the next engineering change (ECN).
   - Suppliers recover their losses by lowering service and quality levels.
   - Suppliers don't give their best cost ideas up-front during design, but save them for the renegotiation.
   - Suppliers don't recover their losses and exit the industry.
2. Global sourcing is a great way to lower costs, but takes huge investments in time and resources before break-even occurs.
3. Exchanges have failed to deliver, any real cost savings and have almost all collapsed.
4. E-auctions are really just another form of win-lose negotiations (There are rare exceptions).

There should be a deep understanding of the trade offs involved in reducing costs of materials and services, and companies need to understand how to help suppliers reduce costs and not simply engage in "margin transfer."

• • •

THE PRESENTATION

The engagement module generally starts out with an over-all presentation to the group. For the most part this presentation focuses on and explains the importance of such issues as the supply chain management process, make/buy policies, the use of volume leveraging, and discussion of the many new and important e-procurement tools available to reduce transaction processing, expand the amount of decision support information available, and integrate the flow of information.

These general topics are usually followed by a look at the state of business between suppliers and the customer company. Receiving special attention are such long-term considerations as greater use of long-term agreements and the potential for more business volume between suppliers and the customer company. Heavy emphasis here is often on these two themes:

- What can we do as a customer to help suppliers be more efficient in their sub-tier supplier procurement practices (e.g. volume leveraging, standardized leadtimes, sub-tier rationalization, material aggregation strategies)?
- What can we do to help us both be more efficient in our procurement and logistics practices (e.g. EDI vs. paper, kitting vs. single piece shipments, supplier-direct shipments to customers, supplier build-to-forecasts)?

The opening presentation also should include a look at the new procurement tools and strategies that are currently being used to achieve cost reduction and an evaluation of their overall effectiveness. Most of all, though, this should be a hard-nosed look at procurement strategies and tools and their potential to help achieve the overall cost reduction target. Real dollar goals should be set and explanations given on how these goals will be achieved

OBJECTIVE AND DELIVERABLES

The objective of the supplier engagement in this module is to define and priortize the supply chain strategies and the e-procurement tools that will be needed to achieve the cost reduction targets. The key deliverables:

- Procurement proposals that, when applied to a component part or part family, will result in a cost savings.
- An idea summary of alternatives in the area of supply chain strategies and e-procurement tools that can achieve quantum cost reductions. However, it is understood that this summary will require significant effort and/or management approval to be implemented.

NEW DIRECTIONS

In setting out the supply chain/e-procurement engagement, new directions need to be taken in the thought process in applying supply chain thinking and e-procurement tools to cost reduction. Among the most fundamental:

- Rationalization of the supply base. Most companies contemplating an ICR program need to begin at the foundation of their supply structure. They need to start figuring out who are their best suppliers for each technology and family of parts. This examination needs to be followed by an inquiry into whether current supplier talents are being used fully and considering whether some help should be given to improve performance.

- Focusing the business on the right suppliers. Supplier partnerships need to be established with selected suppliers and business shifted to them where appropriate.
- Improving key suppliers as they are rationalized. Suppliers often need to be given help in such areas as quality control, delivery, service, cost, and technology integration.
- Integrating suppliers with good ideas into the design, manufacturing, e-business, and product support areas of the company's business.

Much attention in this module will involve dealing with getting suppliers to manage their own supply chains more efficiently. Unfortunately merely nudging suppliers into improving the ways their supply chains are being managed is often not easily addressed. Many small companies simply don't have the time or resources to tackle the sophisticated needs and requests of their large customers.

As a result many of the concerns coming up at this supplier engagement will involve finding ways of teaching suppliers what they need to know and help them to accomplish specific goals that don't involve having to go into a two-year learning curve to come up to the customer's level of accomplishment. The goal is to spot easily transferable information and transfer it. For instance, are there any procedures at the customer company that could be replicated by the supplier for a cost savings benefit and with relative ease?

Where cost reductions in many companies mainly center around negotiated prices, under ICR most cost reductions will be the product of supplier integration into solving long-term issues. The emphasis will be on taking cost out on a long-term, lasting basis rather than through short-term price adjustments. This thinking needs to follow through in drawing up the supply chain/e-procurement checklist of action items to tackle. In any company there are literally hundreds of possible action items that might be tackled. Most, though, fall into these three categories: make/buy, volume leveraging, efficiency improvements.

MAKE/BUY

Decisions about whether to outsource or not are a big issue for all companies and especially so for companies that have done a lot of vertical integration over the years. In growing numbers of companies deep questioning is taking place around what needs to be in-sourced and what should be outsourced. For companies looking for ICR projects, it's fertile ground.

For leaders of this engagement, though, the challenge will often be in pulling suppliers into the spirit of the engagement. The quickest route to getting supplier involvement lies in pointing out to suppliers that there are significant opportunities to increase their business/revenue as well as cost reduction opportunities for the customer.

Once the point is made, suppliers get into the spirit of the engagement and make proposals that often go like this: "We (the supplier) are building four parts for you in this part family, but you still are making three in-house. The processes and the materials are virtually the same. Why don't you let us continue to make our four and take on the three you're doing in-house? With us making all seven, we can lower our cost and we could give you a better over-all price on all seven." The proposal requires no change in design or manufacturing processes. All that's really done is changing the source and lowering the price.

Unfortunately much of what has happened in many companies in the area of make/buy has been less than collegial. Internal turf wars (e.g. VP of manufacturing vs. the VP of materials) have sprung up and often needless arguments have flared up over decisions that were made years earlier under different circumstances. Engagement leaders often need to cut off such unproductive activities at the pass. From the start they need to define what is fair game and what is off limits.

Some companies avoid much of this conflict with the development of a strategic make/buy process that can be effective in deciding competencies—what should be made in-house and what should be bought. Of course decisions at this level often involve such things as core competency, economic capacity, and supplier capability, and have to be addressed at the top level of management. In any case one fundamental question eventually will need to be asked: "Is there a competitive advantage to keeping this technology in-house? Other questions that also need to come under consideration:

- Do we make it because we do it cheaper than anybody else?
- Do we make it because there's nobody out there who can do it so effectively?
- Do we make it just because we have excess capacity?
- If we have the capacity, are we better served by spending our capital on something else?

Other related questions that may come under consideration include such things as what to do with the manufacturing space now that we've moved out? If the company is in a growth mode, there's a ready-made solution—simply use the space for other needs. If the company is in a sustaining or shrinking mode, then it has to do the inevitable: get rid of the space, get rid of the people, or both.

VOLUME LEVERAGING AND/OR ALTERNATIVE SOURCES

Long-term contracting and volume leveraging has a number of aspects that make it a suitable area for potential action items. To begin with, in many cases smaller companies don't have long-term agreements with suppliers. Just by giving a supplier a long-term agreement, the supplier is in a position where it can lower its prices because it now has less of a risk that the customer is going to second-source those parts after six months. We have seen cases, where the supplier can go to its bank and say "I've got this business parts for 5+ years," and bank gives it a favorable loan rate that lowers its cost of doing business.

It's a simple fact of economic life that volume leveraging by part family can play a major role in reducing supplier overhead and component costs—especially where the procurement involves high level assembly. Typically what happens is the supplier says, "I'm building these parts for an assembly. Since I'm already building components 'a" AND "B", why not let me also build component "C" and I'll put all three together and ship you an entire assembly? And because of all this additional busines I can lower your unit cost by X% if you let me build the entire assembly."

Any discussion about rationalization and volume leveraging would be far less than complete without adequately addressing the possibility of second sourcing or transitioning business from the incumbent supplier to an alternative supplier. For some this part of rationalization tends to be somewhat sobering. That's because traditional purchasing in the pre-supply-chain-era (before the 1990s) often wielded the "second source hammer" to beat poor performing suppliers into submission. In some cases it was an idle threat, in others a statement of intent.

In any case, over the past decade, companies have almost universally embraced the concept of "long-term supplier partnerships" and have endeavored to help their partners improve through cooperative efforts rather than always resorting to threats of losing business. The argument in favor of improvement vs. movement presupposes the company has adequately rationalized its supplier base and already separated "the wheat from the chaff" prior to labeling some suppliers as partners and other suppliers as non-partners.

The ICR process is designed for the former category, long term partners. It makes no sense to invest the time and financial resources conducting ICR with a non-partner who is on a "phase-out list." During the preparation module (Chapter 5), the ICR team is required to decide which suppliers and parts should have an ICR engagement. If it is discovered that a part/assembly is being produced by a supplier on the "phase-out list" then the solution to the cost problem for this particular part is NOT ICR, but SECOND SOURCING. In this case the ICR program manager needs to recommend that the materials organization begin identifying and RFQing potential second sources for this part/assembly as soon as practicable. (Note, however, that some parts or assemblies may be with a "source-controlled or single-source supplier." In such a case the ICR program manager needs to ascertain the technical or financial impact of moving this part prior to initiating any recommendations for a second source.

When the option to second source appears to be the best alternative, successful companies have made it a practice to manage the supplier transition as if it were an engineering development project, or "transition program" if the assembly is highly complex or critical. Successful supplier transitions have in place all or most of these elements:

- Project plan. A timeline and detailed action.
- Cross functional team. Part-time or full-time representative from supplier management, engineering, quality, manufacturing engineering as a minimum. Additional team members can be included as the need arises—from production planning, tooling finance, customer service or IT).
- Periodic status reviews.(r)MDNM⁻ Supplier and company team members meet in person to discuss key issues, progress, barriers, and resource constraints.
- Management escalation path.(r)MDNM⁻ When the transition project begins to get in trouble because of a lack of resources or some business issue that the transition team cannot resolve, it is important that management is available for "barrier busting" as the need arises.

Some supplier transition projects are so small in scope that the above is not necessary. Even so, it would be wise to ask the newly selected supplier to do many of the above elements on its side. Also, he should be asked to communicate the project plan and cross-functional team names to the supply chain representative so that he/she can monitor the supplier's progress.

Finally, during the ICR engagement with a "partner" it has been found helpful to have the supplier look into its own supply chain and make some rationalization decisions. There may be second-tier suppliers that are not performing well in cost and quality and your supplier could dramatically improve its cost or delivery performance by rationalizing and potentially transitioning work out of non-preferred sub-tier suppliers.

DOES REAL EFFICIENCY COME FROM E-PROCUREMENT?

Much of the ado surrounding supply chain management and e-procurement tools tends to overshadow their real significance. What gets too little attention is that companies are trying to move in the direction of more collaborative planning. The ultimate state, which is still a few years away for most companies, is for a customer to send an electronic file to a supplier. It immediately gets a file back that bounces off its inventory. It also tells the customer what's available—what it can and cannot promise. It allows the customer to do simulation through the supply chain and ask "what if" questions. This new capability offers a whole range of integrated cost reduction possibilities.

This ability to tie in to electronic commerce is cited over and over by e-procurement consultants. They readily point out how e-procurement can help with elimination of requisitions, purchase orders, and requests for proposal and thereby accelerate the whole process. By predicating future business on use of e-procurement they look forward to an era of highly automated transaction processing and electronic resource planning. For many the instrument in all of this is e-procurement. It can accelerate the use of electronic commerce in procurement and facilitate cost reduction.

But the biggest payoff of e-procurement, ironically, isn't in transaction processing, auctions, or even economic forecasting. It's really quality. With well planned e-procurement systems there are fewer people making errors and others compounding them as they enter and then reenter data into the system. You don't have all the errors of dashes in the wrong place or missing digits in a part description. Quantities in the purchase order and the quantities in the invoice all match up with each other.

Where does all this electronic capability figure in the overall drive to reduce costs? In many (probably most) cases the action items will come in the area of making this new electronic power pay off in reducing supplier costs. Solutions to serious implementation problems are near at hand for many suppliers. The payoff in a supplier engagement session will come as suppliers and customers find simpler, less expensive, solutions to implementation of much of the gear available. Well run supply chain/e-procurement engagement sessions can offer the ideal venue for working out these kinds of problems.

And as companies automate their RFQ, requisitioning, and purchase order processing many no longer need an army of buyers to shuffle paper. Many freed-up workers can be used for more strategic assignments. And in growing numbers of companies suppliers will end up as the planners and buyers who manage the fulfillment of their own parts. The job at a growing number of companies is to train suppliers on how to do just that.

REVERSE ACTIONS AND GLOBAL SOURCING

Reverse or e-auctions and low-cost global sourcing are two potentially powerful weapons against cost, but, like dynamite, they can be and often are extremely dangerous in the hands of untrained or unskilled users. There are e-auction failures in which parts had to be "resourced" back to their original suppliers or "reloaded" back into the factory from which they were outsourced due to substantial quality or lead-time issues.

These failures have been a major argument against the use of reverse auctions and global sourcing to reduce costs. Rather, it is an argument in favor of intelligent application of these cost-fighting tools. Indeed, both tools have been very successfully implemented by a number of world-class companies such as GE, United Technologies, and Ford Motors. The key to successfully implementing e-auctions and global sourcing is found by closer examination of the famous "2x2 Supply Chain Matrix," pioneered by AT Kearney and today used in practically every supply chain textbook in the country.

The 2x2 Matrix can be modified to meet different purposes. In Chapter 7 (see Figure 7-2), we changed the x and y axises to read "savings opportunity vs. risk" or essentially "cost vs. benefit." The more traditional application of the 2x2 matrix is to segregate the supplier base into four groups and manage each group with one of the appropriate strategies shown in Figure 9-1.

The strategic partnerships and key purchases are extremely difficult and potentially disastrous to the business strategy if a second sourcing strategy is pursued. These are the suppliers who should be involved early-on in the design phase of a program providing the engineering team with producibility suggestions before production is initiated. Once the product is in volume production, the ICR process will work extremely well to reduce cost in complex assemblies. Some of the most successful ICR ideas have been generated for strategic products.

Conversely, the commodity and expendables quadrants are relatively easy to second-source either globally or through an e-Auction, since there are numerous potentially viable suppliers for these "non-strategic" components.

There is a simple rule that defines whether a company should pursue global sourcing or e-Auctions (once again these options should ONLY be pursued for non-strategic components in the upper or lower left quadrants of the 2x2 matrix:

Fig. 9-1: The "more traditional" 2x2 Matrix is used to identify the appropriate cost reduction strategy for each product

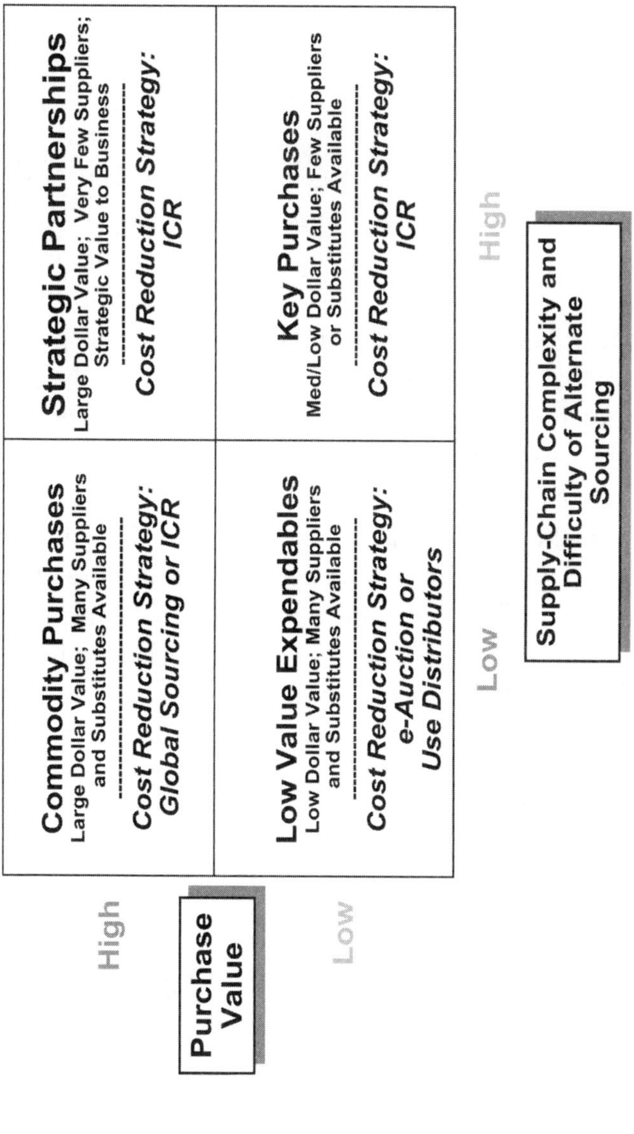

Strategic Partnerships
Large Dollar Value; Very Few Suppliers;
Strategic Value to Business

Cost Reduction Strategy:
ICR

Key Purchases
Med/Low Dollar Value; Few Suppliers
or Substitutes Available

Cost Reduction Strategy:
ICR

Commodity Purchases
Large Dollar Value; Many Suppliers
and Substitutes Available

Cost Reduction Strategy:
Global Sourcing or ICR

Low Value Expendables
Low Dollar Value; Many Suppliers
and Substitutes Available

Cost Reduction Strategy:
e-Auction or
Use Distributors

High

Low

**Supply-Chain Complexity and
Difficulty of Alternate
Sourcing**

**Purchase
Value**

High

Low

Products with high labor content are good candidates for low-cost global sourcing; products with high material content are better candidates for e-auctions or second sourcing.

The reasoning behind the rule is quite straightforward. The benefits derived from low-cost global sourcing are 90% labor-related and less than 10% material related. Typically, international suppliers cannot procure raw materials (or other "true commodity" products, e.g. fasteners, resistors, wiring), much less expensively than companies in the U.S. The global commodity market has roughly equalized the prices of basic material years ago. There are some special exceptions in the case of "native" materials requiring costly bulk transportation and are a purely commercial grade (i.e. cast iron). The primary reason companies such as GE, United Technologies, GM, and IBM source parts overseas is to take advantage of very inexpensive local labor.

One final word on reverse auctions: CEOs love the 30% savings they are often promised. As we discussed in Chapter 1, these numbers are typically "gross" savings, the net savings due to reverse auctions is far less. Most suppliers, on the other hand, hate them. As suppliers view reverse auctions, they create a hyper-competitive, win-lose, environment that can have a very disastrous effect on customer-supplier relationships. For ICR practitioners, the only parts that should be placed on an e-auction block are those of a phased-out supplier, which is due to be exited anyway! In such cases, the e-auction can provide a highly useful tool to accelerate the second source identification and assure that the lowest possible price is achieved.

10

CREATING THE PLAN

EXECUTIVE SUMMARY: At this point the supplier engagement team is deeply involved in implementing and prioritizing supplier engagement recommendations and the process for selecting which proposals get implemented and which get put on hold. To reach this stage, the team has gone through a five-step analysis in which it has:

- Analyzed current manufacturing, design and supply chain processes.
- Defined manufacturing, design, and supply chain alternatives.
- Identified barriers and proposed solutions.
- Prioritized cost reduction opportunities.
- Refined and integrated solutions.

It is now time for these things to begin to happen:

- All the ideas generated at the supplier engagement event need to be identified, summarized, and documented. In addition each idea submitted needs to be written up as completely as possible as the team identifies it.

• A 2x2 risk benefit matrix (Figure 7-2, 7-3) needs to be created and each of the proposed ideas should be plotted. The purpose of this matrix is to provide a logical system for sorting and priortizing the high-value, viable suggestions from the low-value, non-viable ones.

• • •

O NCE ALL IDEAS are identified and summarized they need to be documented. During the manufacturing, design, and supply chain engagements, the meetings may appear to be highly informal. Some people are in a conference room, some are writing things down on the board, but sometimes not everything is being recorded. In addition there often are sideline conversations and hallway conversations; splinter groups that discuss things. This is the time to make sure all the ideas from the splinter groups are recorded in one place. Why is this important? Because if only two persons have heard about an idea and it has not been discussed and doesn't get put into the finalized ICR plan, chances are no part of this idea is going to see the light of day.

It's also important for everyone taking part in this supplier engagement to understand that while this documentation needs to be accomplished as a team, it doesn't occur in a vacuum. No two team meetings are likely to be the same. Each supplier engagement event will tend to be unique. Each set of problems and approaches to those problems will tend to be a little bit different from the others.

THE CLUSTER EFFECT

On the other hand, problems do tend to cluster around different areas depending on how individual companies are set up. Every company has its own "core competences" (those business processes that give each company its own unique competitive advantages) and weaknesses. Manufacturing and design, for instance, often represent the principal areas for cost reduction opportunities. Even small changes in design or in manufacturing procedures can result in major cost reduction opportunities. But in other cases—especially among smaller suppliers—opportunities in the supply chain area are where the real opportunities lie. For example, small suppliers often are at an acute disadvantage in dealing with their major raw materials suppliers who sometimes are hundreds of times larger in size. In such cases significant cost reduction opportunities may cluster around supply chain tools, including the use of such leverage points as the customer company's ability to provide significant negotiating clout for the smaller supplier.

But, no matter how the idea clusters develop it's of prime importance to get the ideas documented and to accomplish this documentation together as a team. In some cases as many as three different teams will have created ideas separately. In other cases as many as three separate teams will have met together in a conference room. As a result, this is often the only time (the last couple of hours of the ICR engagement) when everyone hears all the ideas together. At this stage of the engagement each of the separate breakout teams needs to present its ideas to the entire group.

GETTING A ROUGH PICTURE

After each team makes its presentation, members write down their ideas, put them on flip charts, and present them to all of the other people taking part in the engagement. Each presentation is followed by a critiquing session, where ideas are expanded on in some cases, cut back in others, and discussed in all cases.

Presentation of each idea is followed by the creation of a 2x2, cost vs. benefit matrix (Figure 7-2, 7-3, and 10-1), which is used to develop feasibility rankings for each of the individual ideas. The purpose of these rankings is not to get involved in finite details of how ideas will be put into place, but to develop ballpark estimates of costs and payoff opportunities.

At this stage, rather than haggling over decimal points, team leaders are looking for rounded approximations. For instance, rather than trying to pinpoint precise improvements in quality ("from 55,000 ppm defective to 48,000"), the teams look for quality change estimates in terms of whether quality will improve, decline, or stay the same. Because companies don't have inexhaustible supplies of time or resources it's important at this stage of engagement to continue working with approximations.

THE MATRIX SHORTCUT

In these days of brutal competition companies need to focus their attention on cost cutting and restructuring. What's more, they need to make this focus change in as short a timeframe as possible. Since most companies rarely have excess staff sitting around looking for research projects, we recommend the use of 2X2 matrix graphs. These matrixes will nar-

Fig. 10-1: ICR Supplier Engagement Idea Summary

ROM COST REDUCTION FEASIBILITY RANKING

Idea #	Proposals	Cost Savings		Cost/Risks Required to Implement					
		ROM Savings Potential	Total Savings $K	Quality/ DOC Improved	Risk	Cost to Implement	Time to Implement	Weight Delta	Total Cost (1.00 = Max)
1	D1 - Sample Design Idea	5.0%	100K	3	2	1	4	5	0.50
2	SC1 - Sample Supply Chain Idea	2.0%	75K	3	1	1	2	3	0.25
3	M1 - Sample Mfg/Quality Idea	4.0%	67K	1	2	2	3	3	0.30
4									
5									
6									
7									
8									
9									
10									
11									
12									
13									
14									
15									
	Risk vs. Benefit Criteria -->	1 = <5% / 2 = 5-7.5% / 3 = 7.5-10% / 4 = 10-15% / 5 = >15%		5 = Worse / 3 = Baseline / 1 = Lower DOC	5 = High / 3 = Med / 1 = Low	5 = >$100K / 4 = $50-100K / 3 = $25-50K / 2 = $10-25K / 1 = <$10K	5 = >24Mo. / 4 = 18-24Mo. / 3 = 12-18Mo. / 2 = 6-12Mo. / 1 = <6Mo	5 = >1# more / 4 = 0-1# / 3 = Baseline / 2 = 0-1# less / 1 = >1# less	

row the lists of ideas down to the "vital few" as opposed to the trivial many.

This is accomplished by considering the factors that specifically will need to be considered when the company makes a disposition on an idea. Every company has some kind of process that it uses to approve or disapprove concepts, changes or ideas. At a minimum, an engineering charge request (ECR)can be submitted and routed. Some companies have formal processes. Some companies employ formal suggestion processes that they use with employees submitting suggestions that go through a certain signature cycle—e.g. manager of manufacturing, manager of quality, manager of finance, and manager of purchasing. Each manager has to approve the suggestion and if it all gets approved, then the person who came up with the suggestion gets some sort of reward or recognition.

In any case, the key to fully understanding the significance of the matrix rests to great extent on understanding the process your company uses to approve new ideas. The ICR process needs to be thought of as an idea-generating machine. And once it has generated the ideas the feasibility matrix provides a process for prioritizing them as well as considering an initial "sanity check" of the idea.

Every company's feasibility matrix will be based on slightly different considerations. The sample feasibility matrix and cost reduction implementation chart and matrix in Figure 7-2 and 7-3 show the typical things that most companies are concerned with. They address quality, technical risk, implementation cost, implementation time, and (in this example) weight reduction. (There are many other cost factors that could be covered in the list, such as costs of warranty.)

These factors are combined together to create a weighted overall or implementation cost score. All those numbers are added together to show a grand total. Using the matrix, costs are added together and divided by the total score to put them on a 0-100 scale. By taking all these factors and adding them together no one factor dominates.

In many cases it might be desirable to apply customized weighting. One could, for instance, say time to implement is the most important factor and multiply this column by two and then add everything together. Or, one could say that quality is the most important thing—and multiply that column by three. Different weighting factors can be applied to each of the columns if it's desirable to make the scores reflect your company's individual strategies.

The two cost columns on the cost reduction feasibility chart speak for themselves. They represent total savings as a percent and total dollar savings. More difficult are the estimates of the costs/risks on the cost reduction feasibility-ranking chart. That's because it often is very difficult to tie people down to specific numbers. People capable of giving very good estimates are reluctant to supply absolute numbers. On the other hand, most have few problems dealing with approximate estimates of risks and costs using the 1-5 ranking scale shown on the bottom of the cost reduction-ranking sheet. In fact, where it often gets difficult in dealing with quantities and percentages, it's usually more acceptable for teams to use these rankings.

Real difficulties occur in estimating savings. In order to develop the matrix there must be cost savings numbers. However, suppliers, practically without exception, are hesitant to provide cost savings numbers at this early stage in the cost reduction game. In most cases such reluctance is understandable. Many have dealt in the past with customers who have held them to numbers developed at an early stage of negotiation where they had insufficient time to think cost reduction estimates through thoroughly.

Users of the cost benefit matrix need to remember that this is not a formal RFP or RFQ where the supplier gets two or three weeks to develop a detailed proposal and to run the calculations through its own internal financial system and approval course before providing a bid. This is a "back-of-the-napkin" conversation and it makes some suppliers uncomfortable. To ease any discomfort suppliers are assured that they will not be held to precise numbers. Nothing is fixed in place before a formal suggestion is submitted. However, once the supplier submits the formal suggestion then all estimates become hard numbers.

So after the ICR plan is created, suppliers are given two or three weeks to actually submit a formal proposal for each of its ideas. Again, it's important that everyone realizes that at this stage there is no formal proposal. The purpose of this cost/benefit matrix is the development of an estimate for prioritization and focus of efforts.

The last thing to be completed in the supplier engagement is the 2x2 matrix of all the costs vs. benefits of all the ideas. The software used for this is a very simple spreadsheet, and can be downloaded from www.icrprocess.com. What it says is this idea is clearly out; this one is probably out; but this one is loaded with low-hanging fruit. Translation: It offers a high amount of savings at a low level of risk. And some ideas offer high savings but even higher risk.

In doing this plotting it's important to recognize that risk and time are directly related to each other. An idea that is high risk will take a very long time to implement in any company. Why? Because many people will want to think about it, talk about it, and analyze it. For example, most companies have an approval cycle for ideas. Not just suggestion ideas. They have what is called a configuration or engineering change management (CM) system. When a product is in production, things break and design changes are required, those design changes have to go through the configuration management (CM) system. Ford, GM, GE, and Boeing use them. Every single industrial company in the U.S. has some sort of configuration management system that it uses to approve changes to the design of its products. This change system is only slightly different in most companies and functions basically the same way. If it's a high risk idea, it will likely take a long time to go through the configuration management system.

Quality, for instance, will need to approve a change; manufacturing engineering will need to approve a change; likewise design engineering and finance. (In the automotive industry, finance has to approve every single change to every single component on a vehicle to make sure they understand exactly how the change will affect the cost of a vehicle.)

In other words, Lots of people are going to have questions about changes. So when it comes time for the person from quality to approve the change, if it's a simple change he'll probably sign the change and it will go through. If an idea involves something risky there will probably be demands to consult with the supplier or make a formal proposal. Such meetings can chew up a great deal of time.

THE 2X2 MATRIX IN ACTION

This is where the power of the 2x2 matrix comes into play in sorting out the potential of the submitted ideas. The matrix provides a relatively efficient means for sorting risk/benefit ideas into four piles or quadrants. Relatively high risks need to be identified by virtue of the fact that they will take a long time in moving through the approval process. Other ideas are risky because of high levels of cost they take to implement. A quick rundown of the four quadrants of the matrix:

- **Quadrant 1.** These are the so-called "low hanging fruit." They're easy to do, usually do not require longs waits for approval, cost relatively little to implement.
- **Quadrant 2.** These are called long term, high benefit ideas. In many cases it is possible to get approval, but it may take nine months to a year and a half to get everyone to agree to them.
- **Quadrant 3.** This is probably the most thought-provoking quadrant. It offers low benefits, but also low risks. The majority of ideas submitted will fall into this category. By traditional cost savings standards the savings are relatively good and there usually are a lot of them available. While savings are usually under 5%, they're easy to do. An idea may take only two to three weeks or two to three months to implement, but when all these ideas are totaled up at the end of the year, total cost reductions can add up to more than a single 20% cost reduction.
- **Quadrant 4.** These get crossed off the list immediately. There are few benefits, few savings, yet high risk. To keep the momentum of brainstorming going, these ideas should not be crossed off during the break-out meetings, but during the final wrap-up.

THE ACTION PLAN

From the information developed in preparing the cost/benefit matrix the cost reduction feasibility ranking, and the cost reduction summary for each idea it will be necessary to prepare a three- or four-step action plan. In most cases there won't be time to create a detailed action plan for all of the ideas, but it will be necessary to write down the first two or three steps that have to be followed to ensure the thinking is pointed in the right direction. So, the first two or three actions are the most important. On more complicated suggestions be sure to put down the major barrier(s) to implementation. This requires an explanation of your configuration management, your approval cycle, and which part of your company is going to have the most heartburn with this idea.

If quality has concerns about quality, then the team will need to have a solution to that barrier if the concern is valid. And if quality's concerns are valid, right here try to make an estimate. If quality actually gets worse you may need to reject the idea—or there may, in some cases, be a good reason that offsets the barriers.

In any case, the map has to be pretty complete. This goes back to senior management engagement chapter where we ask top management to assign the weighting factor for the feasibility matrix. Senior management would know what the business situation is.

Depending on what your company has decided, the team will take in order the ideas in quadrant one, two, and three and develop a detailed action plan for each viable suggestion. The action plan does not require a great deal of information. Just four things make up the RAIL (rolling action item list (see Chapter 7):

- What's the idea?
- What's the action?
- Who will do that action (name of person at supplier or customer)?
- Due date?

Most ideas will require far greater detailed planning to be successfully implemented. This implementation plan is beyond the scope of the brief supplier engagement time frame and will be created afterwards. The implementation plan is described in Chapter 11.

11

IMPLEMENTATION
AND LESSONS LEARNED

EXECUTIVE SUMMARY: The rough-draft plan that was created during the supplier engagement needs to be implemented and executed. This includes formally documenting the results of the supplier engagement and sending copies of the engagement results to all the key stockholders—both the active participants in the supplier engagement and the extended team members who were not able to participate but have a vested interest in the process (management, other functions).

Also requiring documentation are the lessons learned for future products and future supplier engagements.

In any case it's necessary to develop a go-forward action plan and assign responsibilities to owners of each of the actions. The typical ICR implementation flow diagram will look something like this:

1. IDEAS/PROPOSALS DOCUMENTE➡

Benefit

Cost

Schedule

Action items

Risk assessment

2. PROGRAM CONCURRENCE

Review team recommendations

Prioritize and approve tasks

Allocate budget/resources

Confirm schedule and
deliverables

Confirm responsibilities ➡

3. YOUR WORK PLAN   ➡

ICR teams document work plans

Assign responsibilities

Establish goals for each part/assembly

Communicate plan to suppliers

4. SUPPLIER WORK PLAN

Document activities needed to
support work plan

Assign responsibilities

Concur on goals, schedule, cost
sharing expectations,

other key deliverables ➡

5. PLAN IMPLEMENTATION   ➡

ICR team:

   Perform analysis

   Procure test hardware

   Perform tests

   Incorporate design changes

Suppliers:

   Optimize mfg. process

   Perform capability assessments

   Provide test parts

   Provide status, data, etc.

6. MONITOR PROGRESS

Periodically review:

   Work status

   Savings projections

   Risk profile

Track:

   Drawing availability to plan

   Test hardware availability

   Part cost (baseline, new

   price, projected savings) ➡

7. CAPTURE SAVINGS	→	8. TEAM RECOGNITION
Change drawings, associated documentation		Publicize team accomplishments
Concur on pricing, terms and conditions with supplier		Recognize supplier contribution
Put new parts on LTA		Share successes with
Document savings>		corporate mgmt. →

9. CAPTURE BEST PRACTICES

Consider implementation on similar products

Determine best method to disseminate results

Consider sharing results with

Center for Process Improvement

• • •

O NCE THE SUPPLIER ENGAGEMENT has been completed, it's very important to strike while the iron is hot. For supplier and customer participants, most events have generated a high amount of enthusiasm and excitement by the end of the process. Typically such sentiments as these are expressed by suppliers: "We never had a customer do something like this before—help us take costs out of our business," or, "Normally they just negotiate our margins away from us."

Typically customers will say, "We never realized the supplier had so many good ideas we could implement on our products." Or, "We never realized there was such tremendous cost savings potential without global sourcing, e-auctions, or (win-lose) negotiating tactics."

TIME TO TAKE ACTION

Therefore, while the ideas are still fresh, you will want to take the approximate savings and the initial implementation plan which was created during the ICR event and take specific actions on specific items within the first two weeks.

Every company will look a little bit different. However, whatever manner each company uses to formalize suggestions and ideas for proposals, that's the process that needs to be followed in the ICR project. Whatever procedure or policy a particular company has for formalizing ideas, suggestions, or proposals should be followed assiduously. Some companies actually have a suggestion form. Some companies have a proposal form that needs to be submitted. Some companies have supplier suggestion programs that need to be followed. So, whatever the existing change management process is, that's what should be done. In addition, suppliers should act on ideas turned up in the supplier engagement. It's very important not to lose any momentum.

IMPORTANCE OF PROJECT UPDATES

What needs to happen next is for your company to set up some sort of status reporting process for the ideas as you convert the ideas into projects. Common sense, as always, should prevail when deciding how much formality should be followed for simple, low-risk ideas, which may simply be "tasks" vs. "projects." So now, what was an idea when it was entered during the supplier engagement now becomes a project (or task for low-risk ideas). And once again, every company does project management differently. Some firms actually have project management software like Microsoft Projects that they require people to follow.

The important thing is that some type of periodic status of the project items needs to be done with your company's management. This could be in the form of a monthly report, monthly review meetings, quarterly senior management briefings, internet-based on-line reports, e-mail reports, etc. Successful companies have found that suppliers participate more readily when they are involved in presenting these periodic reports.

Key suppliers should be encouraged to participate in these meetings to the degree that they present the status of the projects they're working on. If, for instance, the project leader decides to give monthly presentations to management on the status of the ICR project, key suppliers should come in and participate in those meetings and maybe even have those suppliers present the status of the project they're working on—if not every month, perhaps on a periodic basis. The challenge for the ICR project leader has been and will remain the same: keeping resources focused on the project.

REWARDS AND RECOGNITION

The last step in project implementation and without a doubt the most important, is producing the promised results! Having spent this time and money, it's critical that suggestions turn into real money in the form of modified purchase orders, completely finished and implemented engineering changes (ECNs), revised procedures, etc.

After you've collected the money two important things have to happen to ensure future success:

- Some form of reward and/or recognition to the team members that participated should be given—either in the form of recognition by senior management, certificates, plaques, money, dinners—however your company usually accords recognition. This is important for keeping participants motivated.

- Documentation. The step least followed in most companies in the U.S. that have improvement initiatives. There is a need to document the results to develop two "lessons learned" data bases—one for subsequent ICRs and supplier engagements that will be conducted and another for the benefit and future of the products that your company hasn't designed yet. Aim: To prevent repeating the sins of the past.

EPILOGUE

THE INTERNET, lower trade barriers, and globalization will continue to accelerate the need for American companies to fend off ever more sophisticated, lower-cost, off-shore competitors. The apparent dot-com bust seems to have shown, once-and-for-all, that sound business fundamentals of increasing revenues, lowering costs, and increasing profits are not simply achieved by adding an "e-" something to the front of a poorly-conceived business model. Furthermore, the Enron, World-Com, and Tyco fiascos have also shown that a company cannot simply bluff its way to increased shareholder value.

But if the "revolutionary" methods of the recent past don't work, what does? Alas, we would propose a return to the boring, yet proven fundamentals of business success by increasing "real" value for a company's two primary stakeholders: the shareholder and the customer. In Chapter 1 (Figure 1-1) we proposed the value equation as the model for measuring success in satisfying both stakeholders by lowering costs and/or simultaneously increasing product function/service.

	Customer's Definition	**Shareholder's Definition**
Value =	Function + Service =	Profit
	Cost	Invested Capital

Of the hundreds of management fads over the past thirty years, probably the most successful re-engineering processes have been lean manufacturing, Six Sigma, value-analysis/value-engineering, and supply chain/e-procurement. These processes have been proven by hundreds (perhaps thousands) of companies since the early 1990s. The ICR Process is designed to systematically improve both value definitions simultaneously in a rapid, easily repeatable, easily transferable process.

What can be even more appealing to executives burned out by repeated starts and stops, working on the "initiative-du-jour," is the fact that the ICR Process is not a new initiative. ICR is designed to integrate and re-focus a company's pre-existing re-engineering initiatives on the products that need cost reduction the most. ICR will not dilute the already-stretched corporate resources on yet another business improvement fad.

If, after reading this book, you feel your firm could benefit from the use of the ICR tools and processes covered in this book I have put together a very practical, step-by-step "ICR Cookbook." It is available on-line in Microsoft Office format and includes forms, checklists, timelines, sample engagement letters, and blank spreadsheets. In short, the "ICR Cookbook" will enable a company to rapidly make the transition from theory to real-world application. The "ICR Cookbook" is available from www.icrprocess.com or www.integratedcostreductio n.com web sites.

Ron Nussle, Jr.

APPENDIX

THE FOLLOWING THREE CASE STUDIES have been selected from more than 100 actual ICR implementations between 1995 and 2002 and illustrate the use of all three ICR engagement modules in developing quantum strategic cost reductions. The first case study illustrates the use of all three ICR supplier engagement modules—design-to-cost, lean manufacturing, Six Sigma, and supply chain/e-procurement—in helping a supplier dramatically improve its own supply chain costs. Case #1 emphasizes use of ICR in achieving a more cost-effective design and developing more efficient manufacturing processes. Cases #2 and #3 take macroviews of the application of ICR principles. Case #2 examines how ICR identifies cost reduction during the pre-concept (new product) stage. Case #3 explores the application of the "Top Ten" process as a company strives to engage in ICR with all suppliers in an entire corporate-wide commodity over a twelve-month period.

CASE 1: AEROSPACE BELLOWS SUPPLIER (AB)

BACKGROUND: Bellows manufacturing is a technology critical to the control of numerous power generation and transportation industries. Although the fundamental design of the bellows has been in existence for millennia in accordions, pipe organs, and blacksmith furnaces, in the past one hundred years they have been used in the control of devices to convert a mechanical pressure "signal" into a discrete linear movement of a control arm. In the past dozen years bellows have begun to be replaced by digital controls, but in the aerospace industry, with product life cycles of thirty to forty years, the rate of replacement for existing products has been slow. Since the sensitive interaction between the bellows and the output deflection is a function of numerous technical parameters (the bellows material, skin thickness, involute radius, number of involutes, outside and inside diameter, etc.), the ability of a customer to replace one bellows from one supplier to the competitor's design is very limited. Hence, the term "source controlled" is often applied to bellows suppliers, meaning that the engineer specifies that purchasing must buy this particular bellows from the one and only certified supplier. Certifying an alternate supplier after a design has gone into production is very expensive and high risk—especially since the cost of a bellows is only a few hundred dollars and the re-qualification of the design could cost $100,000 or more.

BOTTOM LINE: The supply management organization must work on improving the quality, price, delivery and service of the incumbent supplier, rather than attempt to use strong arm threats to replace it with another supplier.

OVERVIEW: The AB Company (fictitious name) is an autonomous $100 million subsidiary of a $1.5 billion aerospace component supplier with a very long history of supplying bellows to the transportation industry. There are other companies in the bellows industry that cater to the higher volume automotive industry, but AB specializes in the high end aerospace products and has distinguished itself for quality, innovation, and technology. About six years before this case opened, AB recognized that in order to stay competitive, it would have to become more flexible and also make significant progress in "lean manufacturing." The factory floor was modular, mobile, and had "drop lines" to allow the assembly line to be reconfigured in a matter of hours to handle different product demands. AB also had invested very heavily in advance quality methods of statistical process control (SPC) on all its key equipment and operations. AB's technical staff was very deep and accounted for almost 20% of all headcount. Because of the above improvements, AB had been regarded as a preferred supplier with good growth prospects with AlliedSignal.

ALLIEDSIGNAL MATERIALS MANAGEMENT OVERVIEW: In 1992, AlliedSignal was a $12 billion high technology company with three operation sectors in aerospace, automotive, and engineered materials. Aerospace was the largest sector with sales of $4 billion and more than 22 business units around the U.S. During the early 1990s the aerospace industry was in financial turmoil. The nine major U.S. air carriers lost over $13 billion between 1991 and 1993. The impact of these tremendous losses was felt throughout the aerospace industry. The airlines were asking the airframers to cut prices. They, in turn, asked their key suppliers to reduce their prices across-the-board by as much as 25%.

AlliedSignal Aerospace was the third largest supplier to Boeing and was experiencing severe pricing pressures. In April 1992, it hired Ray Stark and Fred McClintock from Xerox to initiate a strategic materials management corporate improvement initiative. The goals were to improve the quality, cost, delivery, and service (QCDS) of its 4000 aerospace sector suppliers. Allied-Signal formed seven sector commodity teams (SCTs) to manage the strategic materials in concert with the business unit tactical materials managers. Each commodity team had a dozen or so full-time, cross-functional individuals with specialties in procurement, quality engineering, manufacturing, product design engineering, and finance.

Each SCT had a specific objective for the QCDS annual improvement of its supply base. While all goals were important, given the current financial woes of the industry, the financial objective needed to be given first emphasis. AlliedSignal stated that before it would sign a long-term agreement with a supplier, the supplier had to make a one-time 10–15% price rebase lining and then commit to smaller year-over-year productivity targets (usually 4–6%).

AB RELATIONSHIP AND NEGOTIATION HISTORY: It was in the context of severe price pressure that AlliedSignal's sheet metal commodity team was assigned the task of negotiating an LTA with AB. Unlike many aerospace suppliers at the time, who were still operating in the "cost plus" mindset that had dominated aerospace for the previous fifty years, AB had already taken bold steps to improve its competitiveness. After nine months of protracted negotiations, the sheet metal commodity team and AB were stalemated. AB could not see any way to lower its prices by even 2% and still make money. AB had already been holding its prices flat for almost six years and using its internal productivity to offset the effects of inflation in labor and raw materials. In fact AB really needed a 5–6% price increase to off-set the effects of recent raw material and labor cost increases. A good customer-supplier relationship was beginning to turn bad and another approach had to be attempted.

NEGOTIATION STALEMATED—ICR BROUGHT IN: Because of the "source controlled" status of AB's bellows, there was not an option of quoting out its business and tryingtofind a lower costsupplier—AlliedSignal had to try to help AB lower its internal costs before AB would be able to lower its prices. During this time, the ICR was just being developed and the sheet metal commodity team (SMCT) agreed to be guinea pig for a first-ever implementation of the ICR process. The SMCT and AB agreed to abide by the output of the ICR project—good or bad.

CRITICAL FIRST STEP: The SMCT met with various members of the business unit technical community who had design responsibility over AB's products. It was agreed that two engineers from the largest two divisions would be available to support the ICR project on an ad-hoc basis. In addition two other buyers and two manufacturing engineers also were identified to work on the team. At three month schedule was agreed upon to complete the process.

PREPARATION FOR SUPPLIER UNDERLINE ENGAGEMENT: The ICR team leader contacted AB and scheduled a two-day brain storming session at AB's facility. It would take two weeks to prepare for the session and both AB and the ICR team would both be preparing information prior to the visit. The ICR team gathered as much technical information about each of AB's twenty-five products and their end-item application as possible in preparation for the supplier engagement.

The engineers gathered end-item performance specifications, bellows quality, and reliability history. The buyers researched the pricing and retooling history of AB's products.

On the supplier side, AB was instructed to pull together manufacturing process routings for each bellows. They were also asked to create a cost breakdown for each of the twenty-five bellows assemblies that showed how much was spent on:

- Direct labor for sub-component details.
- Direct labor for assembly.
- Purchased materials.
- Inspection and testing costs.
- Transportation and storage costs.
- Burden.
- Selling, general, administrative, and other costs.

(Note: since the focus of ICR is NOT on "margin transfer" negotiating away supplier's profit margins, profit should be left out of the cost breakdown.

In addition, AB was asked to provide a spreadsheet that detailed each purchased subcomponent and included:
- Component name and part number.
- Supplier name and location.
- Purchased price.
- Annual purchased quantity.
- Previous year's pricing history, if available.

Finally, AB was busy researching its internal quality history for each bellows to identify any repetitive defects that had occurred.

TWO-DAY ON-SITE ENGAGEMENT
AT ABS FACILITY (AGENDA)

Time	Agenda item	Team members present
DAY 1		
8–10	Overview of ICR process and discussion of ICR goals for 2 day engagement	All
10–11	Plant tour and generic discussion of manufacturing process routing for bellows	All
11–4	Discussion of design to cost opportunities	ICR team leader ICR team engineers (mfg and product design) Suppliers engr. team
4–5	Wrap-up, summary of design-to-cost ideas	All
DAY 2		
8–11	Parallel session #1—manufacturing process review	ICR mfg. engineers Supplier's production, mfg. eng. team
8–11	Parallel session #2—business procurement Supplier's purch. mgr.	ICR team leader ICR team buyer
8–2	Parallel session #3—design-to-cost	ICR team engrs (mfg and product design) Suppliers' engr. team members.
2–4	Integration, prioritization, action planning	All
4–5	Wrap-up, next steps	All

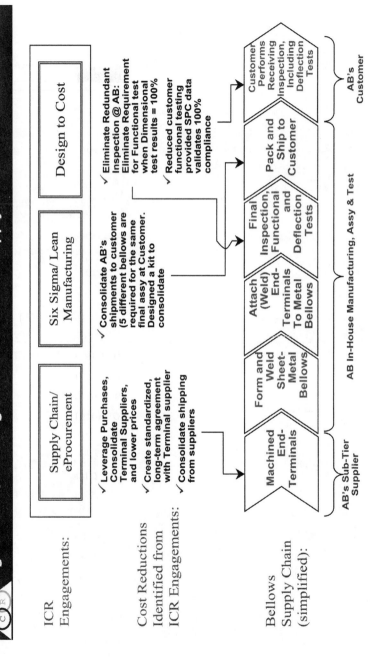

Fig. APP-1: ICR Savings Across AB's Entire Supply Chain

DESIGN MODULE SYNOPSIS: Only three to four ideas came out of the design module. It was estimated that if all ideas were implemented, the total savings would be less than 1.5%/yr. The design-to-cost discussions revolved around a number of redundant inspection requirements in the customer's specification. The customer's inspection required two different techniques for the same parameter of the supplier's component. AB explained that it spent a lot of time conducting the two tests. Because of the stringent quality requirements on these bellows, normally it would have been difficult to eliminate the quality inspection. However, AB was able to produce SPC data that showed that 100% of the parts that passed one inspection standard would also pass the other. An action was taken to review AB's SPC data with the cognizant engineering specialist when the ICR team engineer returned to the plant.

MFG./QUALITY SYNOPSIS: As stated earlier, AB was quite advanced in implementing lean manufacturing principles in its factory. As a result there were only a couple of ideas to reduce the shipping and packaging expense. These were deemed to offer a total savings potential of less than 1%. Since the cost to implement these ideas was quite high, it was not expected that these ideas would be incorporated.

SUPPLY CHAIN/E-PROCUREMENT SYNOPSIS: The surprising golden opportunity was found during the supply chain/e-procurement module discussions. When the team reviewed the spreadsheet of purchased details it became apparent that almost 30% of the cost of the products was in the bellows terminals. These tiny machined fittings on either end of the bellows assembly were purchased from any of a dozen local suppliers on a PO-to-PO basis. Since the unit cost of each terminal was $5 to $25 each, it was not surprising that the local "mom and pop" machining firms did not get very aggressive with their pricing or their processing. The ICR business/procurement team found out that AB spent more than $800,000/yr on these terminals alone. The team came up with the idea of aggregating the entire package of terminals into one supplier and putting together a global RFP package. It was estimated that savings of at least 20% on the terminals could be achieved through this strategy. A 20% savings on 30% of the bellows product cost would yield a 6% overall reduction.

INTEGRATION AND CREATING THE ICR PLAN: The teams came up with a total of fifteen ideas with an estimated total savings potential of 8%. While this was short of the 10% objective, it was significantly ahead of the 5–6% increase in price that AB was requesting. Each idea was packaged together with the appropriate documentation and the ICR team agreed to bring them back to their counterparts and discuss the feasibility of each idea. It was decided that a weekly telecon would be held and in one month the AB team would come to the customer's facility to discuss implementation plans for the approved changes.

ICR IMPLEMENTATION: Immediately after the two-day engagement meeting, the team decided to begin working on the two highest priority initiatives. One of them required a supply chain management strategy to work at the "sub-tier" supplier level. The second strategy was to eliminate the redundant inspections and to consolidate the purchases into one supplier for all terminals.

The following chart summarizes the opportunities generated during the ICR supplier engagement:

For the terminal resourcing sub-project, the process steps would be:

- ID'd another partnering supplier to RFQ
- Contacted personally to inform about opportunity
- Received quotes and analyzed
- Co-developed transition plan with customer, supplier, and new sub-tier supplier.

For the specification modification to eliminate redundant inspection, the process steps are:

- Compare quality data on parts and with or without the redundant inspection
- Modify the specification
- Change the quality and acceptance testing criteria at AB

FINAL RESULTS: 30% savings over previous spend on terminals = 30% x $800K. This process also benefitted AB as it could also help AB improve margins with other customers. Therefore, it was a win-win process and strengthened the relationships of both AB and AlliedSignal.

The engineering specification was changed to eliminate redundant inspections as well.

Since the process was win-win for both supplier and customer, AB agreed to lower prices by an average of 8% across the board. This was especially substantial, given that AB had originally requested a 5–6%price increase. The total gross savings from this ICR project was 13–14% and a project duration of three months. The first ever ICR engagement was a complete success and became the foundation for over 100 more ICR engagements at AlliedSignal, Honeywell and Cessna.

CASE 2: PRECONCEPT DESIGN-TO-COST

Background: Very few products have the technical complexity of an aircraft gas turbine engine (some people call these jet engines, but in reality, a jet or "turbojet" engine is a specific type of the more general category of aircraft gas turbines). A typical gas turbine will have more than 5,000 parts that range from simple sheet metal brackets on the exterior to near-satellite quality rotating bearings held to tolerances 1/30th the thickness of a human hair to single-crystal cooled turbine blades that operate at temperatures above the melting point of the base metal while rotating at the speed of sound. Controlling the gas turbines is an elaborate dual-channel CPU that oversees the operation of more than a dozen electro-mechanical valves, actuators, 50,000 volt spark plugs and pumps based on the signals sent to it from 20–30 pressure, temperature, and vibration sensors in the engine and on the aircraft.

The above technical challenges have been successfully mastered by a half-dozen companies in the world with such household names as Rolls-Royce, General Electric, Pratt & Whitney, and Honeywell (formerly AlliedSignal Engines), and other lesser known names such as Williams International and Snecma. The business jet makers enjoyed enormous market expansion over the 1990s. The market doubled in size to over $45 billion (total for 1990–1999) since the 1980s and is projected to double in size again to $80 billion in revenue between 2000 and 2010. However, global competition has also affected this market. To wit: Almost a dozen new business jet models were launched during the 1990s. This is more than twice as many new models as the large commercial transport segment (Boeing and Airbus class) fielded during the same time period. During this period, one of the gas turbine manufacturers decided to design a completely new gas turbine with cost targets 30–40%

below any model ever produced, (For the sake of confidentiality, the company will be designated "BJE" (Business Jet Engine) and the engine, itself, the BJE-1).

BJE COMPANY OVERVIEW: At this time of the case BJE had more than $1 billion in annual sales and a substantial share of the business jet market. BJE had been an inovator in the business jet market, but recently had begun to lose some critical competitions because of the lack of new engines to offer the market. BJE's competition had invested more than 15% of its revenue over a half-dozen years to develop a suite of new centerline engines. Unfortunately, BJE had not done so, and by the time it decided to launch its new product it was estimated that BJE was almost eighteen months behind its competitor in developing an engine for the highest growth sub-segment of the business jet market. Its main competitor had used design-to-cost techniques and low-cost global sourcing strategies in its recent engines and BJE believed that the competitive engine was 20–30% lower in cost than any product BJE currently offered. Thus, the target—to be 30–40% below any current BJE model—was aimed at giving BJE a 5–10% price advantage over the competition.

BJE-1 PROGRAM OVERVIEW: The objective of being 30–40% below the current product line was daunting enough. It was compounded by the fact that BJE was eighteen months behind the competition and the BJE-1 would have to be developed and certified faster than any product in the company's history. To minimize the timeline a parallel technology validation effort had already been conducted to test out some higher risk technologies before they were incorporated into the baseline design. The design team had broken the BJE-1 down into eight modules or sub-systems and assigned a complete project team for each module. Each module team had a project engineering manager and a cross-functional team representing each functional area—design, materials and process engineering, manufacturing engineering, supply chain, and various technical specialties. In addition, there was a separate test engineering group tasked with designing, fabrication, and flight-testing the planned eighteen engines. This would become the largest program in BJE's history with almost 300 full-time engineers assigned to the project for a 12–24 month program.

PROJECT NOT MEETING COST TARGETS—ICR brought in: four months into the 18-month program, the baseline technical configuration was not even close to accomplishing the 30-40% reduction. In fact, the baseline design was only forecasted to be 5-10% less expensive than current product offerings. It was time for serious re-evaluation of the project and its ability to accomplish its objectives. It was decided to launch a 6-8 week "Tiger Team" tasked with developing an entirely new product design that could achieve the 30-40% cost bogey.

ICR PROCESS OVERVIEW: Program management engagement became the critical first step. Developing an entirely new product architecture for the BJE-1 in eight weeks would require the highest priority in the entire corporation. This was accomplished by a memo from the president of the company being sent to three of his peers in other divisions to support the effort. It was decided to set up a separate line-item budget for the eight week, $250,000 tiger team.

PREPARATION FOR THE ENGAGEMENT: After the initial memo was sent out by BJE's president, 101 engineers were invited to the two-day, off-site engagement event. Given the limited time frame, and since no suppliers had yet been selected (the detailed design was not even started) it was decided that it would be impossible to actually bring in suppliers. Instead, supplier engineers were brought in from each commodity team. Each commodity team engineer had already conducted dozens of ICR events with their respective suppliers, so they had a tremendous amount of first-hand knowledge of suppliers' cost drivers and manufacturing capabilities.

Since this was a pre-concept design, it was not possible to have actual hardware photos, or even completed drawings. Rather each module team leader, plotted out 200% size (4 ft. x 8 ft.) module assembly concept drawings. In addition, each team leader created a typical bill of material for a similar design, which listed the most likely materials and suppliers for the major components in each module. Since each module had between 300 and 500 parts, it was impossible to go through each during a 2-day brain storming session.

Two-day brainstorming agendas (engagement module): The agenda for the 2-day off-site engagement is shown below. Note the parallel sessions. Two modules were conducted simultaneously in different conference rooms. The format for each brainstorming session is listed below this overall agenda.

Time	Agenda item	Team members present
DAY 1:		
7–8	Overview of ICR process discussion of ICR goals for 2-day engmt.	All
8–12	Module #1 design-to-cost brainstorming session	Module #1 team: Team leader. Engineers (mfg., product design and specialty), Commodity team engineers (max: 10–15 people total)

Time	Agenda item	Team members present
DAY 1		
8–12	Module #2	Module #2 team
12–5	Module #3	Module #3 team
12–5	Module #4	Module #4 team
DAY 2		
8–12	Module #5	Module #5 team
8–12	Module #6	Module #6 team
12–5	Module #7	Module #7 team
12–5	Module #8	Module #8 team
5–6	Wrap-up, next steps	All

BRAINSTORMING SESSION FORMAT: Each brainstorming session lasted four hours. The format was classic "nominal group technique" with a design twist.

Duration (Mins)	Step name	Who participates
30 min	Module overview	Project team leader

Module design concept explained. Targets explained (performance, cost, weight # parts, etc.)

3 hrs Brainstorming sessions: 10 min./ part x 20–30=3 hrs. total

2 min/ "walk around"	Sub-component	Each of the 20–30 major design specialists

sub-part assemblies is explained, described. Similar-to hardware available

| 5 min. | brainstorm | All |

all team members use Nominal Group Technique (a.k.a. "post-it notes") to write down potential design ideas

| 3 min | synthesis | All |

Each idea discussed, part duplicates discarded, definition expanded

Following the completion of each brainstorming session, all the ideas were written up and summarized for the executive debrief.

ICR IMPLEMENTATION: After the 2-day off-site there were more than 400 ideas generated. During the next 6-7 weeks, each of the eight module teams was assigned to "run to ground" each idea and categorize it as either:

- **Low risk**—incorporate into the baseline design.
- **Medium risk**—incorporate into the baseline design, but run parallel path technology risk assessment.
- **High risk**—Do NOT incorporate into baseline design, but begin technology development program in parallel and, if successful, incorporate into a later revision of BJE-1. It was expected that the BJE-1 would be the first in a product family of potentially 3-4 similar designs. Therefore, there would be the opportunity to incorporate additional technologies at a later date.

At the end of the seven weeks, a series of successive reviews was conducted to validate the feasibility of the 400+ ideas. Each module team had to meet with 2-3 levels of technical management to review their Low/Med/High assessment of risk. At the end a final "blue ribbon review" was conducted with retirees, Ph.Ds, and other very senior individuals who could provide a very realistic assessment of the likelihood of successful implementation.

FINAL RESULTS: After completing the 2-dayoff-site engagement and the 6 week validation and final blue-ribbon review, the team categorized the suggestions into low, medium, and high risk. As it was stated earlier, only the low and medium risk ideas were incorporated into the baseline configuration. For comparison purposes, the "Legacy Design" (20-yr old product that was being replaced by BJE-1) is also shown:

System	Total ** Engine Cost ($K)	% **	Comments
Legacy Design"	$125	+125%	
BJE-1 baseline desgn	$100	—	Pre-ICR prod cost, design.
Low risk config	$85	-15%	Selected config.
Medium+low risk	$70	-30%	Med. risk "potential"
High+med+low risk	$55	-45%	Future opportunities (2–3yrs)

** Note: The "%s" are accurate, but the "$s" are fictitious to protect proprietary engine cost information.

As can be seen, the low risk configuration was selected, as the go-forward design. Since the medium risk configuration allowed substantial benefits, a parallel path design effort was begun to merge these ideas into the product as soon as they were tested out. Furthermore, a "high-risk" technology demonstrator program also began. It was expected that these concepts would require 2-3 years to bring to production readiness and they would be incorporated into a later variant of the BJE-1 ("BJE-2").

CASE 3: ENGAGING WITH ALL SUPPLIERS IN A COMMODITY

BACKGROUND: During the mid-1990s AlliedSignal was in the midst of implementing a corporate materials management process. Today the term would be "strategic sourcing" or "strategic supply-chain re-engineering." Allied Signal's experience was one of the first examples of what hundreds of companies have found over the past decade after their first two years of launching a strategic sourcing program...the law of diminishing returns sets in!

Bad news; strategic sourcing always follows the "law of diminishing returns": Hundreds, perhaps thousands of companies have launched strategic sourcing programs since the mid-1990s. The process most companies follow is quite similar:

- Analyze current spend and categorize by commodities, suppliers and products.
- Identify "quick win" savings opportunities.
- Consolidate purchases into a small, preferred supply base.
- Renegotiate long-term agreements with these preferred suppliers to achieve year-over-year price reductions.

Many companies have learned that it is relatively easy to accomplish the above 3-4 steps over the first 18 to 24 months of a newly launched strategic sourcing process. Inexperienced CPOs may think it is possible to do this year-over-year forever, without end. Seasoned CPOs have learned that after 2-3 years the "low hanging fruit" of leveraged negotiations has been picked. Suppliers' margins have decreased to such an extent that they are unwilling to provide the same level of cost-reduction as they were during the initial long-term agreement negotiations.

What then? AlliedSignal found that to accomplish cost reductions in year two, three, and subsequent years, it was necessary to actually reduce the supplier's own costs (not profits) in partnership with suppliers. The ICR process was launched simultaneously with a half-dozen supplier cost reduction processes to address the fundamental cost elements of AlliedSignal's suppliers.

ICR PROCESS OVERVIEW: AlliedSignal's seven sector commodity teams (SCTs) each operated autonomously and were each in various stages of maturity in their approach to supplier cost reduction. The sheet metal commodity team (SMCT) was very successful in its first two years of existence in leveraged procurement. In the first year more than 12% average cost reduction was achieved. The second year saw a decrease to less than 10%, and by the third year when the ICR process was launched, 4-6% was going to be an aggressive target.

The SMCT total supply base numbered over 300 suppliers and the 80/20 rule applied, with approximately 80% of the spend occurring in the top 20% of the suppliers. The top 50 suppliers represented 74% of the total spend.

It was decided that a massive effort would be made to conduct day-long ICR events with all 50 SMCT preferred suppliers. A schedule was created to visit all 50 suppliers over a 12 month period. The supplier engagements were prioritized by spend and savings potential and the on-site engagements were scheduled based on priority and geography to minimize travel and logistics costs. Prior to launching the effort it was necessary to garner support for each engagement from the product engineering and manufacturing engineering organizations. A cost/benefit analysis was conducted and the potential savings was explained to the senior management of the technical staff before finalizing the schedule. Senior management decided it was NOT possible to have technical resources "on-the-road" for 30 weeks in a row and a modified schedule of 3-4 supplier engagements per month was realistic. At this revised rate, it would require 15 months to accomplish the 50 engagements.

PREPARATION FOR ENGAGEMENT: After some initial data-mining, the SMCT found that each of these 50 suppliers provided dozens—up to hundreds—of parts. It was not feasible to re-engineer 100% of every supplier's parts, so once again the 80/20 rule was followed.

"TOP TEN" PROCESS IS BORN: By analyzing the supplier's spend, it was learned that 90% of the 50 suppliers had fewer than 10 part numbers driving 50-80% of their spend. Therefore, the SMCT decided to go only after the "top 10" or fewer parts at each supplier (500 parts total).

Three preparation steps: To ensure successful engagements, the SMCT followed three steps prior to arriving at each supplier's facility:

- **Step 1**: A letter was sent out by the director of the SMCT informing each of the 50 suppliers that a team would be arriving in the next few months to conduct the on-site engagement (a sample letter is available on www.icrprocess.com. Whenever a supplier's executives would visit the SMCT, the supplier was asked to support the Top Ten process, even if the engagement was 3–6 months away. Not one of 50 suppliers was unwilling to participate, since the ICR process demonstrated a true willingness to have a "win-win" partnership on the part of AlliedSignal.
- **Step 2**: One month prior to the engagement , a letter was sent to each supplier listing the Top 10 parts and describing

the ICR agenda that would be followed. A copy of the letter was sent to the AlliedSignal engineering and manufacturing engineers who would attend. Both supplier and AlliedSignal engineers were asked to gather drawings, specs, part history (rejects, cost trends, raw materials. etc.).

- **Step 3:** One week prior to the engagement, a telecon was conducted with the supplier, the SMCT, and the technical team. The telecon discussed the agenda, purpose, attendees, and finalized logistics and filled in any gaps in the historical or technical background of each of the top ten parts.

SUPPLIER ENGAGEMENT FORMAT: Since it was decided to conduct more than 50 engagements, the technical resources would be strained to conduct a 2-3 day event at each supplier. It was decided to focus efforts on a more streamlined one-day session with a focus on design and manufacturing improvements. With a tremendous amount of preparation ahead of time, the ICR team arrived and after a brief plant tour and explanation, moved to a conference room where each supplier already had drawings marked up with suggested improvements. The ICR team was able to make it through all 10 parts at every single one of the 50 suppliers over a 15-month period. As noted above, a small number of suppliers had only 4-5 parts that accounted for 80+% of their sales to AlliedSignal. In these cases, the process focused on a smaller population of higher-potential parts.

INTEGRATION AND CREATING THE ICR PLAN: As is almost always the case, each part has its own "story." Even the simplest part, such as a bolt, often has more than a dozen different features described on an engineering drawing/specification.

FEATURES ON A BOLT

Length	Diameter
Thread depth and type	Number of threads
Head diameter	Head length
Number and size "wrench flats"	Chamfer at bottom of shank on the head
Edge breaks at the head	Raw material type
Straightness of shank	Roundness of threads
Perpendicularity of the shank to the head	Packaging and labeling requirements

If a supplier is serious about reducing cost, it is certainly possible for a supplier to identify improvements to any one or all of these features. Each one of these suggested changes would need to be looked at by the product design engineer to ascertain whether these changes would adversely impact the end-item's reliability, serviceability, or performance. Cost reductions at the component level could easily be outweighed by increased warranty costs for the end-item if no analysis is conducted.

A bolt is among the simplest examples of a part design. Since SMCT parts were made up of welded assemblies and very few "simple-stamped" sheet metal parts, most of the "Top Ten" parts were components or sub-assemblies with at least a dozen items on their own parts lists (fasteners, materials, specialized fittings, welded-on or cast features, etc.). With a complex welded assembly and over a dozen individual items on each higher level part, there were hundreds or even thousands of features that could be reviewed on each part! For this reason, it is easier to see each part as a "project" with individual actions requiring reviewing each part and feature change.

ICR IMPLEMENTATION: Unquestionably, the most challenging aspect of the "Top Ten" process was keeping track of the status of the various actions required to accomplish cost reduction on 500 (50x10) "projects." A Microsoft Access database was created to log all of the cost reduction ideas and the actions, accountable parties, and due-dates required to "approve" each idea on each part. Weekly telecons were established with the various product engineering groups to review their actions, status, and estimated completion dates. Monthly status reports were created and once/quarter an overall status was presented to AlliedSignal"s VP of materials.

FINAL RESULTS: Overall, the "Top Ten" process was highly successful. The 50 supplier engagements were accomplished in 15 months. More than 500 individual parts were reviewed for cost reduction and more than 400 had cost reduction opportunities. The average savings identified was 7–12% per supplier, with many potential savings of over 15% on individual parts.